THE EMOTIONAL REHABILITATION OF THE GERIATRIC PATIENT

The Emotional Rehabilitation
of the
Geriatric Patient

By

KURT WOLFF, M.D.

Director, Professional Education and Research
Veterans Administration Hospital
Coatesville, Pennsylvania
Associate Professor of Psychiatry
Thomas Jefferson University
Philadelphia, Pennsylvania

CHARLES C THOMAS · PUBLISHER
Springfield · Illinois · U.S.A.

Published and Distributed Throughout the World by
CHARLES C THOMAS • PUBLISHER
Bannerstone House
301-327 East Lawrence Avenue, Springfield, Illinois, U.S.A.
Natchez Plantation House
735 North Atlantic Boulevard, Fort Lauderdale, Florida, U.S.A

© *1970, by* CHARLES C THOMAS • PUBLISHER
Library of Congress Catalog Card Number: 79-126495

With THOMAS BOOKS *careful attention is given to all details of
manufacturing and design. It is the Publisher's desire to present books
that are satisfactory as to their physical qualities and artistic possibilities
and appropriate for their particular use.* THOMAS BOOKS *will be true
to those laws of quality that assure a good name and good will.*

Printed in the United States of America
I-1

To
MY WIFE

INTRODUCTION

Dῦ瑞NG THE PAST TEN YEARS, child psychiatry has become a growing and desirable medical psychiatric specialty. Many training centers emphasize training in child psychiatry as one of the requirements for board certification in psychiatry. Geriatric psychiatry, on the other hand, is still a neglected area of specialization and training. It is practiced in only a few training centers and then primarily as a sideline. This is most unfortunate because the number of geriatric patients is continuously increasing.

What are the reasons for this lack of interest in gerontology in psychiatric training centers? Some psychiatrists feel that elderly people are not approachable by psychotherapy because of the inflexibility of their character and because of their memory defects. Occasionally an elderly physician identifies with a geriatric patient only to become eventually depressed himself. Other physicians grow definitely hostile towards the older patient because they themselves are still deeply involved in their own unresolved "Oedipus complex." Thus, their resistance to helping the geriatric patient may well reflect their hostility against their own parental figures. Another important issue involves the physician's attitude toward old age generally and death particularly. If the physician is afraid of growing old himself and finds this thought depressing, he will not successfully be able to treat elderly patients. It is axiomatic that the physician be able to understand the emotional problems of the aged and to convey kindness and hope.

In addition, the psychiatrist must have a good knowledge of general medicine as well as skill in dealing with social, economic, familial and cultural processes, since they all have the greatest influence on the geriatric patient. As Birren,[1] Busse[2] and the author[3] have pointed out, the study and treatment of the geriatric patient require a multidisciplinary approach involving the handling of biological, sociological and psychological factors. The elderly patient simply cannot be understood and helped unless all these features have been dealt with and the "total personality approach" has been put into practice.

A few years ago a new term was introduced and widely popularized—the "generation gap." This term describes differences in attitudes, values, feelings and behavior between the young generation and the elderly. Thus, youth is viewed and has come to view itself qualitatively different from the rest of the population. I believe, however, that younger and older persons should not be considered as separate entities. Their problems are connected and interrelated. We cannot expect to come near to a solution for closing the "generation gap" without studying these interrelationships. As for the older citizen, we must keep trying to understand his needs. Critical comments in terms of inflexibility, rigidity and so forth are not fruitful unless more knowledge can be obtained about the biological, sociological, and psychological problems of the elder generation, about their motives and attitudes. Value judgments are not likely to lead to problem-solving behavior either by the person involved or by the society in which the person lives.

The problems of our elderly citizens are indeed important and very complex. As Bortz[4] has correctly emphasized, we need a cultural reorientation. This reorientation involves shifting from a youth-oriented society to a society where family and group values are more stressed, where change is emphasized in terms of biological rather than chronological time; from a sickness-oriented society to a health-oriented one, with less concern about acute disease and more interest in long-term disorder, and where, finally, problems involving retirement are to be replaced by thoughts of a "second career."

The aging citizen indeed has become a national and international problem. A recent article published in *Aging*,[5] the magazine of the United States Department of Health, Education and Welfare, has pointed out that by 1985 the older population is expected to increase about 40 per cent to twenty-five million people. Every tenth person in the United States at the present time is 65 years old or older, a total of almost twenty million men and women. Thus far in this century, the percentage of the United States population aged 65 and over has more than doubled, from 4.1 per cent in 1900 to 9.5 per cent in 1968. In the same period of time, the number of people over 65 increased more than sixfold, from three million to more than nineteen million in 1969. Women now outlive men. At present, the life expectancy at birth is 73.8 years for females and 66.7 years for males. The life expectancy for women is still increasing faster than for men. More than three of every ten persons aged 65 or over live within the four most populated states in the United States: California, New York, Pennsylvania and Illinois, each of which has more than one million older people. These factors are even more remarkable when we consider that the average life span about two thousand years ago (in Rome) was 22 years; in the Middle Ages (in Great Britain), it was 33 years; and in 1900 in the United States, the life span was 49.2 years. Sheldon[6] made a critical review of statistics on elderly persons in the United States and throughout the world, which revealed that the underdeveloped countries are those with "young population," while those with an older population are the industrialized countries in western Europe and their offshoots in other parts of the world. While Brazil, Egypt and Ceylon, for instance, have a relatively greater percentage of young people, France, Germany, Great Britain and the United States count a relatively greater percentage of older people.

Generally speaking, at the present time about 30 per cent of all new admissions to state psychiatric institutions are 60 years of age and over. In most psychiatric state institutions throughout the United States, more than 45 per cent of the patients are over 60 years of age. Even in "younger countries," like Australia, this trend of an aging population is evident.

This book will review many conceptual views and treatment methods of the biological, sociological and psychological aspects of the elderly, both inside and outside hospitals, and will point out both long-established and more recently developed fruitful ways of prevention, treatment and rehabilitation of the aged. It is hoped this material will be of value to those interested in the problems of the aged and that it will give some direction for a better understanding, support and guidance of this large segment of our population.

Kurt Wolff

ACKNOWLEDGMENTS

I AM INDEBTED and deeply grateful to Karl Menninger, M.D. (The Menninger Foundation), William Rottersman, M.D. (formerly at the Menninger Foundation), Harold E. Himwich, M.D. (Galesburg State Research Hospital, Ill.), William S. Middleton, M.D., and O. K. Timm, M.D. (formerly at the V.A. Central Office, Washington, D. C.); to F. S. Cornelison, Jr., M.D. (Thomas Jefferson University, Philadelphia) for giving me moral support during my career in the United States; to David Cohen, Ph.D. (Chief, Psychology Service, V.A. Hospital, Coatesville) for editorial advice on many of my papers; and finally to Miss Virginia Domblesky of the V.A. Hospital, Coatesville, for secretarial assistance.

K.W.

CONTENTS

THE EMOTIONAL REHABILITATION OF
THE GERIATRIC PATIENT

PART ONE

I

BIOMEDICAL ASPECTS OF AGING

Various biological factors contribute to the senile changes. According to some investigators, genetic factors are involved. Senescence depends on progressive morphogenic changes which are not "inherent" properties. Experiments with animals prove this theory; for instance, offspring from young mothers live longer than those from old mothers. Furthermore, there is an increase of longevity cumulative over successive generations. Matings between long-lived mice have shown that longevity is a characteristic determined in part by parental influences. Longevity depends also on the species. Reptiles and fish increase in size during their total life span. In contrast, warm-blooded animals grow rapidly during early life and then decline in size after maturity. The length of life depends on body temperature as well. When the body temperature of insects is held slightly elevated, they die earlier than cold-blooded animals, which maintain a uniform temperature. Furthermore, life is shortened by overfeeding in silkworms, rats and mice, while restriction of caloric intake extends their life span. In recent years increased interest has been shown concerning the effect of radiation on the life span. It has been found that sublethal doses of radition, for instance, resulted in premature aging in rats.

What actually is the aging process in our organs and tissues?

BIOCHEMICAL AND PHYSIOLOGICAL STUDIES

The majority of gerontologists agree that a sharp distinction should be made between the *process of aging* and the *state of being aged,* or senility. Lansing[7,8] considers senescence to be a process of progressive loss by the adult of the ability to live, while senility is a state of adulthood in which the ability to live has been reduced. Lansing points out that after the age of 40 the individual is prone to accumulate fat, the physical capacities are reduced, vision is deteriorating and there is a lack of adaptability to environmental changes. The elderly person has learned to compromise. He fatigues more easily and does not generally force issues. While mortality from infections has considerably decreased in old age, chronic rheumatic arthritis and osteoarthritis, cardiovascular disease, cancer, and diseases of the nervous system become predominant and represent a serious problem of treatment and rehabilitation. Yet, problems connected with aging can and do occur in young adulthood. Arteriosclerosis is not solely limited to advanced age, and calcification of the aorta can, indeed, begin at the age of 20. Other investigators believe that age pigments are an important characteristic of the process of aging, but already at the age of 7 the first traces of yellow pigment can be observed in several types of nerve cells in men. They can be found in the liver, the adrenal glands, the cardiac muscle, the anterior pituitary glands and the nerve cells. Acid-fast age pigments appear frequently in human cardiac muscle as early as the age of 20 and increase thereafter. Lansing[8] believes that calcium may play an important role in establishing the aging process because calcium lowers cell permeability.

H. E. Himwich and W. A. Himwich[9,10] give much importance to the fact that after 40 years of age the basal metabolic rate, or the oxygen consumption of the entire body gradually falls, with a more rapid rate decrease after 80 years of age. The Himwichs have observed a gradual increase of water at the expense of solid elements in old age, the metabolism of the brain declines with the basal metabolism and the brain appears to shrink. Buerger[11] found a definitive decrease of the size of the brain after the age of 30. Heinrich[12] pointed out that, while the ventricles of the brain enlarge in old age and the total volume of cerebrospinal fluid increases, the brain tissue itself contracts. The Himwichs find that both the white and the gray matter of the cerebral cortex show an accumulation of moisture in old age, and they believe that the gradual increase of water at the expense of solid elements, along with morphological alterations, may represent the basis for mental impairment of the elderly. Very interesting are the studies of Buerger[13] in regard to the chemical changes of the brain substance in old age. He comes to the conclusion that there is a definitive decrease of the total brain lipids from 78 to 90 years. Generally, the amount of proteins and especially the values of glutamic acid, glutamine pyruvic acid and alpha-keto glutamic acid in the brain tissue diminish. Furthermore, Nikitin and his co-workers' studies[14] suggest that protein, although decreasing in quantity, remains unchanged as to its amino acid content.

It is a fact, however, that the regressive changes in the brain substance itself are not always associated with clinical manifestations. The question as to why the decreased metabolism, because of augmented cerebral vascular resistance and dependent upon retardation of blood flow, is not compensated by reduction of cerebral vascular resistance when the blood pressure falls cannot as yet be answered. Therefore, many authors believe that besides the parenchymal damage which causes alteration in the brain cells, still another factor must be present which causes the phenomenon of aging. This could be some kind of toxic product of still unknown origin influencing the function not only of our brain cells but also of the cells of our organism as a whole. Experiments, then, done during recent years by the Himwichs,[15] suggest that generally in old age nitrogen and phosphorus substances decrease in the brain, while sulfur-rich substances increase at the age of 90. The lipid and total protein fractions decline and some "undefined lipid," perhaps the lipochrome of the yellow plaques, is augmented. The cells and axons of the central nervous system dwindle, and the aqueous element of the brain expands. Ventricles enlarge, and the brain shows parenchymal atrophy. Kety[16,17] affirms these findings and states the loss of neurons, the progressive deterioration of certain essential cellular components, and the decrease in neuronal interconnections and interactions are important factors inducing the process of aging. Cerebral oxygen consumption, according to Kety, expressed as milliliter of oxygen utilized per 100 gm of brain substance per minute, shows a gradual fall with advancing years. For Kety, the rapid fall in the circulation and oxygen supply for the brain from childhood to aging is at the base of all the other chemical, biological and functional changes.

As Sobel[18] points out, "the accumulation of lipofuscin—a lipoprotein material commonly designed 'age pigment'—has been known for many years." In humans it accrues with advancing age in liver, nerves and heart. It is unclear, however, whether this is the result of the passage of time alone or whether it is due to the experiences to which the organism has been exposed during this time.

Furthermore, during the aging processes, body tissues accumulate and concentrate at least twenty metals. Age changes are being sought also in enzymatic activity and in the coding of information for protein synthesis. The need for "adaptation" may result in marked variation in protein synthesis.

Schwartz[19] describes the importance of amyloid infiltration of many organs and tissues—particularly of the brain, the cardiovascular system and the pancreatic islet—which, according to Schwartz, occurs more frequently than atheromatous lesions of arteries.

Lowry and Hastings[20] observed that extreme age results in an increase in water, sodium and chloride and a decrease in acid-soluble phosphorus and potassium in the skeletal muscle. Interpreted histochemically, age has resulted in a near doubling of the extracellular fluid without change in water or potassium concentration in the cell. The moderate increase in lipid concentration is of interest, since like the change in extracellular fluid, the change with old age is the reverse of the change with growth. There is a suggestion that the extracellular compartment contains a lower proportion of solids in old age. In general, then, in aging as in growth, the muscle undergoes definite alterations, but the composition of the intracellular phase changes comparatively little.

Freeman[21] states that a variety of body functions show a loss of over 25 per cent of capacities in general aging trends with allowances for a number of wide divergencies for individuals. In almost every instance, cellular effects have a predominant influence. Reductions in physiological capacities include loss of effective cells, regression in certain but not all properties of these cells, and the tendency to the progression of physiological changes to a pathological status because of a combination of extrinsic and intrinsic effects. Although cell numbers, particularly certain types, are essential to the explication of senescent mechanisms, cell changes and acquired states of organization and regulation are necessary to the comprehension of the nature of the aging process. The key to the situation is the metabolizing cell mass. Its determination can be effected directly or indirectly by certain measurements: (1) total body water consisting of the extracellular and intracellular functions in which the reduction of the total amount is correlated with the loss of cell numbers; reduction in body intracellular water; (2) decrease in body potassium; (3) reduction in bone mineral mass; (4) increase in body fat; and (5) decreases in aggregate body metabolism (as oxygen utilized in terms of body weight in time), caloric requirements, pulmonary, renal, cardiac functions and glucose tolerance approximate closely to changes in active cell mass.

Atrophy is commonly considered an attribute of many old tissues. The skeletal muscle, for example, in a very old individual is greatly reduced in mass in comparison to its bulk at the height of vigor. It is not entirely clear how much of this decrease in total mass is due to actual loss of fibers and how much is to be accounted for by a decrease in their average size. Extensive measurements demonstrate the occurrence of hypertrophy in the surviving fibers of the ocular muscles in the eighth and ninth decades, but these studies were purposely made on the eye muscles in which activity is not greatly restricted in old age. It is reasonable to believe that the fibers of larger leg muscles, for instance, undergo considerable atrophy from disuse in later life.

Shock[22,23] confirms the importance of the decreased basal metabolism in old persons. Reduction in total metabolism is simply a reflection of the reduced number of metabolizing units (cells) present in the organism of the elderly person. Decreased skeletal muscle efficiency, decreased muscle tone and actual muscle atrophy are, Shock suggests, a consequence of advancing age. This concept of decreased metabolic processes of our body cells with advancing age becomes evident by partial involution of the thyroid gland in old age. Dryness of the skin and scalp, loss of hair, lowered resistance to infections, weakness and atony of the skeletal muscles, reduced speed of mental performance, and slower reaction time gives proof of it.

Verzar,[24] in his paper entitled "The Growth of a New Science," states that N. W. Shock (Baltimore) and M. Bürger (Leipzig, Germany) compared the carbohydrate metabolism in apparently healthy people of different ages with glycogen production, glucose absorption and the effect of insulin in the elderly to find out if senile diabetes exists. Shock furthermore made studies on respiration and the biochemistry of the blood plasma and showed the homeostatic regulation by way of the respiration and the kidneys becomes less efficient in later life. Other studies are being made on changes in the fat metabolism and muscular efficiency with increasing years.

Shock[25] made interesting observations also on the homeostatic mechanisms* in the aging body. According to this author, the internal temperature of elderly persons is maintained within the same limitations as those in the young (under resting or basal conditions). Skin temperature only is slightly lower in older persons than in young subjects owing, chiefly, to the diminished circulation in the skin of the aged. There is evidence, however, that the response to high or low environmental temperature is less effective in the old than in the young. While young persons show little change in rectal temperature, in aged people a fall of 0.5 C to 1.0 C during exposure is frequent. It is generally believed that aged individuals show a greater increase in oxygen consumption than the young. The former reveal impairment in their ability to adjust to increased

---

* Cannon defines homeostasis as a term to designate maintenance of a steady state of equilibrium of the cellular environment throughout the body.

environmental temperatures, demonstrated by heat prostration, which happens more frequently among the old than among the young. It is well known that the death rate from heat stroke increases considerably after the age of 60. Furthermore, in elderly subjects there is less increase in pulse rate during the influence of heat than in the young, and the ability to dissipate excess heat is lowered. This is caused by partial disappearance of skin capillaries, atrophic, dry, rough and unelastic skin, with reduced capacity of the skin capillaries to dilate. Many studies have been made in regard to blood pressure elevation in old age. According to Shock, under conditions of standardized exercise, which does not represent all-out exertion for younger subjects, the increment of blood pressure is significantly greater for the old than the young.

McFarland[26] has suggested that hypoxia and aging cause similar changes, according to studies on (1) light sensitivity and dark adaptation, (2) critical flicker frequency, (3) effect of glare, (4) auditory sensitivity and (5) mental functions. The causes could be related to reduced supply, delivery, diffusion or utilization of oxygen.

Geschickter[27] comes to the conclusion that aging may be due to a gradually increasing discrepancy between the demands of specialization by the tissues and the available metabolic support. Since most tissues are dependent upon their blood supply for nourishment, and since natural aging is a slow and progressive decline of function, these regressive changes in the tissue are, in general, correlated with changes in the blood supply. If diminution of the blood supply proceeds too rapidly, the tissue will undergo a form of atrophy which may be classed as accelerated aging. On the other hand, if damage to the tissue exceeds that to the blood supply, resolution, organization and fibrotic repair of regeneration will replace the aging process. Natural aging, therefore, presupposes a certain degree of correlation between parenchymal and vascular changes, with the rate and amount of tissue lost being roughly proportional to the declining vascular status of the individual organ affected.

Geschickter is of the opinion that a number of metabolic

factors can accelerate the aging process. The most readily demonstrable are those arising from exogenous deprivation, such as starvation, low protein intake, and lack of fat or lack of vitamin B complex absorption in the bowel. Endogenous disturbances of the metabolism are more numerous and more intricate in bringing about accelerated aging. The most universal endogenous metabolic factor is interference with the vascular supply. Since we have found acceleration of the aging processes in joints of subjects of advanced renal disease, it is probable, according to Geschickter, that vascular disturbance operates both through the production of hypoxia and the diminished removal of metabolic waste products.

Barnes, Busse and co-workers[28] have made special studies on brain wave changes in elderly persons and found a slowing of the alpha rhythm in normally functioning elderly persons and an even greater slowing associated with psychologic decline. In addition, a special focal disturbance has been found in "normal" subjects over the age of 60, as well as in subjects suffering from organic brain disease. In 80 per cent of the cases these dysrhythmias are located in the left temporal area, most often in the anterior temporal region.

Busse and Obrist[29] report that approximately one-third of the population 60 years or older have deviant electroencephalograms of a focal type consisting primarily of slow waves. The disturbance is usually maximal over the anterior temporal area and occurs most often on the left side of the brain. Although it has not been proved, it seems probable that this pattern is of vascular origin; and although no consistent correlation has been established with physical or psychological impairment, it might be assumed to have some effect upon the functioning of a person.

As a normal adult advances through life the aging process is clearly reflected in the EEG. Anterior temporal foci, found in 36 per cent of elderly seniles, first appear in middle age. Diffuse fast activity is frequently found in the normal aging female. Fast brain rhythms reach a peak during the late middle years in women and decline somewhat during senescence.

It appears also that the amount of antibodies, agglutinins and precipitins in the blood is decreased in the older age groups. It is a well-known fact that the functional properties of the sexual organs diminish in old age. Furthermore, the sensory apparatus of the whole organism is in decline. Visual acuity is reduced, partially because of either physiological hyperopia in old age, glaucoma, cataracts, or damage to the retina of the eye. Impairment of hearing, especially for high-pitched sounds, can be due to otosclerosis and occurs frequently.

Muscular tone, coordination of the muscular system, and speed of muscular movement frequently show alterations or impairments. In most organs cells are replaced by connective tissues, causing either defective function, atrophy or other degenerative changes.

Stieglitz[30,31] is of the opinion that one of the most important contributions of modern medicine was a conceptual clarification concerning the child as not merely "a little man," but as an organism which presents structural, functional, chemical, metabolic, nutritional and psychological characteristics peculiar to his biological age. In a similar way, old people, too, are structurally, functionally and mentally different persons than they were in younger years. Stieglitz is in favor of a special approach to the geriatric problem which considers structural, functional and chemical changes by themselves. The structural changes involve an atrophy of parenchymatous tissues and, in consequence, an increase in interstitial tissue. This does not mean, however, that structural changes are always associated with functional impairment. The normal functional reserves are very great and are not exhausted easily. Naturally, renal, hepatic, pancreatic or thyroid atrophy affects the whole organism. Histological and histochemical studies of the individual tissue cells alone do not resolve the problem regarding the origin of senility. Cellular proliferation declines with old age and necrocytosis (atrophy of cells resulting in their death) increases. Functional changes concerning the pulse rate, arterial tension, body temperature and water content are an indication of an altered equilibrium. In regard to speed of response and effectiveness, the aged have more difficulty in maintaining a uniform body temperature and tolerating cold. Perhaps they are more sensitive to a hot environment because of partial atrophy of the sweat glands.

It is well known that either increased intake or deprivation of sugar is badly tolerated by elderly persons. An imbalance in the hydrogen-ion concentration of the blood frequently gives rise to serious disturbances because in the older person the homeostatic equilibrium of the organism is more easily disturbed and returns to its normal level with more difficulty.

MEDICAL AND NEUROLOGICAL OBSERVATIONS

Freeman[32] has given special consideration to the factor of endocrine mechanisms in the aging body. This author observed evidence that the pituitary-adrenal mechanism responds with average expectancy, even in the very old. In a study of adreno-cortical response to adrenocorticotropic hormone (ACTH) in young and old men, it was found that there may be a decrease in ACTH production with age. Furthermore, it has been shown in humans that the production of gonadotropin is greater in aging women than in young ones and that hypophysial changes are not marked in senescence. In the thyroid gland, however, the uptake of radioisotopic iodine is decreased with age. In older men there is usually a decrease in the concentration of serum protein bound iodine (PBI), which is less marked in women. The parathyroid glands were found to be very re-sistant to changes associated with aging. On the other hand, the pancreas appears to be more susceptible to changes in elder-ly persons. Deficiency of the pancreas in the production of in-sulin induces to a decreased glucose tolerance of the diabetic type. Significant modifications in adrenocortical response could not be revealed. In older men, according to Freeman, no di-minished adrenocortical activity under ACTH stimulation, whether in degree, duration, metabolic or hematologic effect has been demonstrated. Most scientists working in this field appear to agree that gonadal failure has remained the only endocrine alteration characteristic of old age, and the ovary may be completely worn out and unable to respond to specific pituitary stimulation. Therefore, it is generally believed that in the aging body there is a persistence of the integrity of the pituitary-adrenal mechanism, there is maintenance of the functional capacity of the catabolism-mediating glands in contrast to a progressive loss of capacity in the glands with anabolic activities, and there is a definite reduction in the biological and chemical reserves by which anabolic effects can be accomplished.

McGavack[33] states that functional alterations are commonly seen in middle or late middle life, that time of life conventionally associated with the beginning of aging. Reference is made to the gonads, the thyroid, the pituitary and the adrenals, in which anatomic and physiologic changes occur as a function of time somewhat in the order mentioned. While no part of the body and no bodily influence are without effect upon these glands, their interlocking activities are as important to the changes of aging as are their individually specific functions. Both genetic and environmental influences predetermine the actual rate at which a given individual grows old. While the encoding upon the deoxyribonucleic acid (DNA) of the germ cell can probably not be altered once laid down, a knowledge of its nature may permit the altering of environmental influences in such fashion as to minimize adverse effects and further beneficial aspects of the individual inheritance. Studies of the gonadal and thyroidal function of more than two thousand subjects during the past twenty-five years lead to the belief that much can be done to improve the lot of the oldster, although we probably cannot prolong his life, according to McGavack.

The neuropathological aspects of aging have been studied extensively by Berry.[34] According to Berry, it is a fact that if we adhere to a biologic definition of aging as the progressive loss of functional capacity of an organism after it reaches reproductive maturity, the nervous system begins to senesce when it becomes less capable than in earlier life to deal with the problems with which it is faced. We must further differentiate the inevitable and universal, normal, or physiologic effects of the passage of time from those pathologic, secondary, accidental or individual effects which accelerate or aggravate the aging process.

Involutional changes of brain and other tissues are commonly reflected in atrophy of the organ. Diminished bulk presumably reflects the loss of tissue, especially neurons, in the central nervous system.

Nerve fibers in a peripheral nerve trunk show a 37 per cent decrease between age 30 years and old age. The commonly observed loss of muscle power reflects decreased bulk of muscle tissue, although there is little decrease in the speed of impulse along a nerve fiber. Other tissues show varying degrees of loss of substance.

Changes in the spinal cord with aging, beginning in the fourth decade of life, have been described. These include arteriosclerosis, thickening of meninges, loss of myelin in the lateral and posterior columns, ependymal hypertrophy, presence of corpora amylacea, overgrowth of glia, and the lipid degeneration of neurons.

Atrophic, pigmentary and degenerative cellular changes of the central nervous system, although characteristic of old age, are not diagnostic, according to Berry. Individual variations are marked.

Schlezinger[35] points out that in elderly people there seem to be certain inevitable changes from a neurologic standpoint. Included among these alterations are the following: (1) the eyes show a tendency toward diminution in the size of pupils as well as an impairment of accommodation and a reduction in adaptation to darkness—there also appears to be some limitation of convergence and, not infrequently, a limitation of upward gaze; (2) the ears show some impairment affecting the hearing of high notes; (3) a slowness in reaction time is confirmed by special testing; (4) a slight impairment of memory for recent events is common in the older person; (5) a reduction in agility, noted in the gait as well as in the performance of complex actions, is usually evident in the later decades; and (6) impairment of vibration sense in the lower extremities has become generally accepted as a development in the older person.

According to O'Leary[36] the norms for neurological evaluation of aging subjects differ from those for average adults in several respects. As aging progresses, the individual becomes less adept at fine movements. Habitude may be characterized by semiflexion at the principal joints, resistance to passive movements, and slowness of willed activities, giving the impression that significant involvement of the basal ganglia exists. However, a general outfall of neurones may lead, in age, to a predominance of the flexor musculature, and the infirmities of joints and tendons also contribute to the change in posture. The same musculoskeletal infirmities may contribute to the shortening of stride and unsteady gait which lead eventually to a shuffling, propulsive wide-based walk. The musculature may be hypertonic and the knee jerk overactive during normal aging; ankle jerks may be much reduced but are rarely absent unless that finding has clinical significance. Again, vibratory sensibility is often diminished so significantly in the distal parts of the extremities (particularly the legs) of old people that this test loses some of its value in detecting evidence of posterior column involvement, such as occurs in combined sclerosis. When it is only reduced or perverted (as, for example, being experienced as hot or cold) in the very old, the observation has debatable significance. Small pupils and slowness of pupillary response, amounting to sluggishness, may be due to atrophic change in the iridial musculature.

Certain neurological symptoms are encountered, commonly enough, in aging patients. Among these are syncopal attacks and vertigo. Less frequent, and usually associated with significant organic cerebral pathology, are senile tremor, Parkinson's syndrome, chorea and convulsions.

Wexberg[37] made a comparison of neuropsychiatric conditions in American Negroes and whites and came to the conclusion that there are three cerebral conditions in which there is a definite difference as to racial incidence between Negroes and whites. Cerebral syphilis is by far more frequent among whites than among Negroes. The same holds true for senile dementia and for Parkinson's disease but not for cerebral arteriosclerosis. Not only the racial factor but also nonspecific exogenous factors ought to be considered to explain the lower incidence of certain cerebral diseases in Negroes as compared to whites. It is a general experience among populations of the same racial extraction that, for instance, general paralysis is more frequent among highly civilized groups than among primitive ones—thus, the southern Negro seems to be comparatively protected. The same seems to be true for senile dementia. It is not a question of whether the Negro brain is less susceptible to senile processes, but it is a question of how the total personality of a particular social and cultural type stands up under the wear and tear of civilization.

Whereas a nonspecific exogenous (cultural and social) factor appears to be responsible for the difference of incidence between Negroes and whites as far as senile dementia is concerned, the same does not hold in arterosclerotic disease of the brain, which is not so much a disease of the brain as a disease of the blood vessels.

HEREDITY

The hereditary influence on the aging process has been studied by many investigators. Kallman[38,39] divides the heredity influences on senescence into three categories. The first group is due to gene-controlled deficiency states, physical or mental, which arise before the senescence period but alter the "adaptive plasticity" of aging persons. To this group belong the major psychoses, specific metabolic disorders and various types of subnormal intelligence, emotional instability, schizoid personality traits and complusive drinking patterns. In most of these conditions the genetic components tend to complicate the process of aging. Not much is known about the cause of failure in adaptive defenses in elderly patients of this kind. The second group is composed of gene-specific disorders limited to the senium, including Pick's, Alzheimer's and Jacob-Creutzfeldt's diseases. In these sicknesses, which are conducive to gross or relatively circumscribed brain lesions, the hereditary factor might be a specific factor in their development, a theory proven in Pick's disease, which is caused by a simple dominant gene. It appears also that hereditary factors are of importance for patients suffering from essential hypertension, cerebral arteriosclerosis and senile dementia. Kallman considers also the influence of hereditary factors on the specific disturbance of the lipid metabolism (primary hypercholesterolemia), which permits early vascular changes. However, hereditary predisposition can hardly be the only or the most important factor in early arteriosclerosis. Senile psychoses may be better understood by taking into account many factors leading to an emotional maladjustment before senescence, rather than a single hereditary factor.

A third group exists which has a more or less specific hereditary component with respect to longevity and general survival. To this group belongs a more or less unspecific degree of hereditary influence regarding the age factor of the parents. In addition, the obvious similarities in regard to the physical and mental process of aging, social adjustment, intelligence and its rate of decline in identical twins are found in this third group.

More recently the somatic mutation theory has been emphasized, especially by Curtis.[40,41] According to this author, it is quite impossible to cover the vast literature on the subject or discuss even a fraction of the theories of aging. It seems reasonable, according to Curtis, to define aging as a biological process which causes increased susceptibility to disease. Even cancer and atherosclerosis would then be considered biological phenomena separate from the phenomenon of aging. First is the group of theories which postulate the accumulation of deleterious products of metabolism as a cause of aging. Certain products such as collagen accumulate in some tissues and give these organs the appearance of old organs. Next are theories of "wear and tear." Each stress to which an organism is subjected takes it toll, and the organism finally wears out. The cells of an organ are endowed with a certain complement of enzymes at the time the organ is formed, and when this complement is used up the organ can no longer function properly. The third view—and the most important view, according to Curtis—is the mutation theory. According to this theory, somatic cells of the body gradually accumulate deleterious genes by mutation, which cause the cells, and thus the organism, to function less efficiently.

Comfort[42] has accumulated data indicating that with increase of stress, life expectancy decreases and aging is accelerated. Selye and Prioreschi[43] have also emphasized the importance of stress in aging but, according to Curtis, without supporting experimental data. For instance, experiments with nitrogen mustard (or tetanus toxin or other chemical agents) administered to rats did not cause aging. Factors, either spontaneous or artificial, which increase the mutation rate also decrease the life span. Correlations between the development of chromosome aberrations (and presumably somatic mutations) and life span are very impressive.

According to Jarvik,[44] we may suppose that the time sequences involved in aging are programmed into the individual at birth, like the predictable time sequences of other changes associated with the growth cycle. Aging phenomena occurring after the reproductive period cannot be regarded as adaptive processes determined by natural selection. Genes influencing aging exert their major effects earlier in life and only secondarily influence aging and longevity. Further, it is possible that the psychological changes in the senium are associated with morphological changes in the brain, particularly in the glial elements.

Possible changes in immunological status with advancing age have been described by Walford.[45] According to this investigator, two possible mechanisms for aging on an immune basis can be suggested. The first is mitotic inhibition. There is ample evidence of slowing of the mitotic rate with age. The number of mitoses per unit area in various organs clearly decreases with age. The second possible mechanism of aging on an immune basis concerns the idea that antibodies may act as cross-linking or denaturing agents.

Reichel,[46] on the other hand, considers various biological aspects of the aging process. According to Reichel, aging has multiple causes. First, there is the initial genetic variability in the organism. Second, there is the destructive effect of the environment. Third, there is an accumulation in the somatic cells of changes, mutations or local chemical damage. These changes incapacitate or kill individual cells and eventually cause a decline in physiological capacity.

THE DIETARY PROBLEM

Of very great importance for understanding the aging process is the dietary problem. Stare[47] has made extensive studies of nutrition and has come to the conclusion that the need for a sound nutrition in the elderly differs only slightly from that in younger adults. A good dietary plan for the elderly should include fewer calories.

This investigator found a mean caloric intake of 2500 calories sufficient for men 65 years of age and over, and 1700 in women in the same age group. Fifty per cent of the men and 47 percent of the women are more than 10 per cent above their optimal weight, and the excess of caloric intake replaces muscle tissue by fat. Such an accumulation of fat affects the organism unfavorably and leads many times to a disturbance of the circulation and gastrointestinal activity, with a decrease in longevity. Stare recommends, for elderly people, a relatively high intake in proteins, meat, eggs and milk in order to maintain nitrogen equilibrium. Where aged persons cannot afford such a diet financially, a mixture of cereal products to which amino acids, such as lysine, are added are to be preferred. Lack of sufficient proteins in the diet can cause hypoproteinemia with the symptoms of senile pruritis, bedsores, wounds that do not heal and chronic eczematous dermatoses, which we find so frequently in senile patients. Moreover, the phenomena of fatigue, edema, anemia, and lowered resistance to infections in many old people might be related to a low protein intake. Therefore, old people should reduce their caloric intake, especially in regard to fat, and instead take more proteins.

According to McCay,[48] mechanization has decreased human

movement so that the typical older person can live with very little compulsory exercise. Hence, his intake of foods in terms of energy usually will amount to only 1500 to 2000 calories, or about half the intake of an adult or a large youth. With this lowered intake of food, every effort must be made to insure high quality in terms of essentials, because the need for such elements as calcium does not decline in proportion to the need for energy. In fact, the requirement for calcium rises in old age and may exceed the amount needed at any other period of life. Likewise, the need for vitamins and proteins seems just as high in old age as in middle life.

The second great hazard in later life is the temptation to consume foods that provide little besides energy. The two that create the greatest danger are alcohol and sugar. The next two, in order of importance, are cooking fats and white flour. With the exception of alcohol, these substances all offer the additional temptation of being cheap sources of energy. They are not cheap if they lead to years of ill health in later life.

The old person, more than any other, needs to shop for natural foods that are both economical and rich in essentials. Some of these foods are dry skim milk, soy flour, dry brewer's yeast, wheat germ, potatoes and whole wheat flour. The best meats are those rich in vitamins, such as heart, kidneys and liver. Eggs are nearly complete, and the current fear of them because of their cholesterol content is not justified.

Since the older person may be dependent upon foods which are ready to eat, he should give special attention to basic products, such as bread. Bread can be made from excellent formulas containing milk, wheat germ, soy flour and yeast, or it can be made very poorly of white flour with few additions. What is true for bread is also true for breakfast cereals and sweet baked goods.

The older person can help his own diet by mixing dry skim milk or dry yeast into his foods. He can keep a sugar bowl on his table filled with powdered bone meal and another filled with yeast or wheat germ. These supplements can be eaten at each meal. Milk is probably the best food for later life. Tests with animals have indicated that they can be reared and kept for the whole of life upon no other food than fresh milk. Older as well as younger people can profit by the use of more milk.

Among the plant proteins, the best is that from soy beans. This can be purchased as flour and used in many foods.

Brewer's yeast is one of the richest natural sources of both protein and water-soluble vitamins. It can be taken suspended in water just before meals by those who tend to become overweight. It can be used to lessen the need for insulin by diabetics. It may help prevent constipation; but it may cause trouble for those afflicted with gout since it is rich in purines.

Nutrition during later life requires regular study by every individual to insure sound food habits and to avoid the pitfalls of alcohol, sugar and fat.

THE "STRESS" THEORY

In many publications Selye[49,50] stresses the factor of close interrelations between the "general adaptation syndrome" and aging. This author believes that older people can, at first, get used to the alarming effects of cold, heavy muscular work, worries and so on. Although, after prolonged exposure, sooner or later all resistance breaks down and exhaustion sets in. Something gets lost or used up during the work of adaptation. Energy is consumed in the process of adaptation. This energy is completely different from the caloric energy we get by eating. Although we do not know exactly what this energy might be, research along these lines could advance investigation into the fundamentals of aging. This adaptation energy depends to a great extent on our genetic background. We are able to draw thriftily upon this energy reserve for a long but monotonously uneventful existence, or we can spend it lavishly in the course of a stressful, intense, more colorful and exciting life. Rest cannot entirely restore lost energy for people after exposure to very stressful activities. Reserves for adaptability cannot be completely replaced, and each exposure to stress leaves scars which influence our life. Aging, according to Selye, is due to a deficit in adaptation energy during life. Nobody, this author states, ever dies of old age, because all the organs of his body wear out and wreck the whole human machinery in consequence. This seems to be the price human beings pay for the evolution from a simple cell into a highly complex organism. Unicellular animals never die, because they divide and their parts live on. According to Selye, greater importance should be given to the factor of "wear and tear." This investigator states that there is a great difference between physiological and chronological age. One person can be much more senile in body and mind, and much closer to the grave at 40 years than another person at 60 years. Selye believes that true age depends largely on the rate of wear and tear, on the speed of self-consumption. To him, life is essentially a process which gradually spends the given amount of "adaptability energy" that we inherited from our parents. Vitality is like a special kind of bank account which you can use up by withdrawals but cannot increase by deposits. The person's control over this most precious fortune is the rate at which withdrawals are made. The solution, evidently, is not to stop withdrawing, for this would be death. Nor is it to withdraw just enough for survival, for this would permit only a vegetative life—worse than death. The intelligent thing to do is to withdraw generously but never expend wastefully. Selye explains furthermore that the belief of restoration by rest after exposure to very stressful activities is a false one. Experiments on animals have clearly shown that each exposure to stress leaves an indelible scar because the animals are using up reserves of adaptability which cannot be replaced. It is true, according to Selye, that immediately after some harassing experience, rest can restore us *almost* to the original level of fitness by eliminating acute fatigue. But the emphasis is on the word *almost*. Since we constantly go through periods of stress and rest during life, even a little deficit of adaptation energy every day adds up. It adds up to what we call aging.

The stress theory has not been proven experimentally to be of greatest influence on the factor of aging yet, but according to Whipple,[51] a great variety of psychological stresses (including the burden of everyday living) in addition to chemicals and diseases might be the cause of imbalances of function in many organs, making them susceptible to weakening by somatic mutation. Clinical experience, however, appears to confirm the stress theory at least partially, as has been pointed out by Wendkos and Wolff[52] in recent publications on the emotional origin of angina pectoris.

II

THE SOCIOLOGICAL ASPECT

THE SOCIOLOGICAL ASPECT of aging is, I believe, connected to a high degree with three important problems: first, voluntary or involuntary retirement; second, our cultural attitudes toward elderly people; and, finally, the feeling of economic insecurity.

Badly managed retirement is, indeed, according to my own observation, a frequent precipitating factor causing emotional upsets in elderly people which often lead to hospitalization. When older persons do not have hobbies and interests, developed in earlier years, which are able to occupy their time and thus their minds after retirement, they are unable to relax and to enjoy life. Too much inactivity makes them feel useless and superfluous, causes them to concentrate their interest on physical sicknesses, which can create many psychosomatic complaints and depressions. Retirement often causes a severe loss of self-esteem. To lose one's goal in life means for many old persons the end of all hopes and of life itself. Many old people have for years held their mind and their body together by compulsive work, are not accustomed to relaxation and, not knowing what recreation means, have in later life a complete breakdown of their physical and mental health. They can experience sudden and severe confusion and disorganization. They are really "lost" in the true and symbolic sense of the word.

Elderly persons must, therefore, have something to retire to. To find suitable hobbies and interests for them, to help them relax and be less anxious, to help them to "recreate" a new life is, indeed, one of the most important goals of our preventive treatment for emotional disorders in aged persons.

Burgess and co-workers[53,54] have made an extensive study of the occupational differences in attitudes toward aging and retirement at the Industrial Relations Center, University of Chicago. They come to the conclusion that there is a great difference in retirement planning between at least two occupational levels, the upper-level occupational group and the manual worker. The supervisory-professional group shows a more favorable attitude toward old age and retirement planning. The manual worker reveals greater difficulties in the areas of mental outlook toward old age, financial planning, family and friends, meaning of work, retirement planning, social adjustment and job satisfaction. Burgess and his co-workers have come to the conclusion, therefore, that retirement programs should be designed differently for these two occupational levels. The upper-level occupational groups need a greater opportunity to reinterpret and to assimilate their knowledge, while another program is needed for the manual worker, who frequently cannot find in the concept of retirement and old age a promise of a meaningful and well-rounded life.

Richardson,[55] in a report on retirement by personal interview with 244 retired men in Scotland, tried to define in more detail the reasons why people retire, especially on medical grounds. He also made an investigation regarding the reemployment potential of these retired men and the use they have made of retirement. Over one-half of the group had a disability of occupational significance. The most common disabilities were heart disease, arthritis and bronchitis. Retirement had been due most frequently to ill health or action by the employer, but the cause of retirement varied with age and social class. Half of the retired men had not found a contented way of life. In contrast, however, almost all those doing part-time work were satisfied with their compromise between full-time employment and complete retirement. The main activities of the retired men were helping at home, walking and gardening. The prevalence of true hobbies was low.

White[56] points out that to anyone who feels that his work is useful to society, retirement is repugnant. To anyone who finds activity necessary to health, retirement presents a critical problem in rearrangement. To a factory worker who has been tied to a machine for most of his life, retirement may seem the long-awaited release from bondage. To a creative person, retirement seems physically impossible, even if it were to prove financially feasible. To those who are emotionally unequipped to face the facts of old age, retirement is frightening—a symbol of approaching death. To anyone who feels that making money is the most fun there is, retirement sounds dull and empty. To anyone who has always gone somewhere in the morning, even to a place he has not particularly liked, retirement seems like the removal of the most steadying thing of all, his destination. To the person whose family cares and responsibilities have increased with the years, whose dependents have multiplied, retirement—and the reduction of income—seems utterly bewildering. To the person who has become emotionally attached to an organization, retirement seems like compulsory divorce from a beloved spouse, an act of incredible cruelty. To a great many millions of workaday toilers in the American vineyard, who keep their health and do their jobs, retirement comes like a slap in the face; it carries the implication that their powers have waned, their day is done and their countenance is no longer a welcome sight around the shop. Since there are almost as many problems of retirement as there are people who work for a living, it is no wonder that the subject is much in the people's minds in this age of industry, in this land of extreme busyness, where the very thought of anyone's dropping out of the parade is disturbing if not degrading.

Shock[57] has given much thought to the problem of old age and retirement. He concludes that, to keep old people in emotional health, flexible plans for retirement have to be worked out. The status of the person's physical health remains an important factor determining employment, but emotional factors, too, have to be given much more consideration. This author advocates a plan of gradual retirement over a period of years whereby the older worker would be able to develop other interests or hobbies outside his job. In this way a better adjustment to the status of retirement can be achieved. It seems that in the age group of 65 and over, more women than men remain employed and that women in the higher age group usually outlive men.

Donahue[58] came to the conclusion that many old people over 65 are still competent and able to do most work efficiently. Compulsory retirement at 65 or beyond is not the solution to the problem. Therefore, job counseling services for older workers and community programs to help them to retain their social usefulness are recommended.

Streib and Thompson[59] found that, in elderly persons, their concept of anticipatory retirement is of great importance. These authors suggest that retirement should be considered as a process which goes on over a period of time and only ultimately may lead to a state of being "retired." Problems pertaining to adjustment precede retirement by a considerable period of time. These ideas are furthered by Tibbitts,[60] who believes that we should consider the person's adjustment at the age of 50 or even earlier. We then would be able to assess more precisely the individual's capabilities to adjust to retirement.

Giberson,[61] in a valuable paper, points out that for the industrial worker, retirement looms ahead of him as a dread thing, the end of his importance to himself and to his company. He fears the incompleteness which his remaining years promise him. He is utterly unprepared for leisure. He is inarticulate about this, of course. His fears may come out in catankerousness and officiousness, and he may try the patience of a whole organization before he retires.

This author recommends a gradual retirement plan which would acclimate the worker to his new leisures and new horizons because of the medical dangers of sudden retirement—the nonadaptation to new routine, the lethal cessation of physical activity. Mentally, too, there is the danger of an aggravated irritation, of childish and unsocial petulance, that may transform a fine citizen into a liability. These dangers can be avoided by an active program set in motion years before retirement. The worker's imagination could be kindled by the possibilities of the leisure opened up for him upon retirement. Leisure clubs might be organized, for instance, where all the colorful details of fishing, gardening or useful social activities are emphasized and made available.

A good program should include some concrete evidence of the esteem and respect in which the older employee is held. In the interests of general morale, and in the efficient use of its resources of skill and judgment, industry itself should arrange some means of keeping in direct contact with its retired employees. Such precautions as these are not impractical; they are merely prudent savings of morale and skill. While the elderly worker might exhibit some loss in coordination and in physical endurance, these are frequently compensated by a gain in judgment and in working skill. Slight adjustments in working conditions and in speed rates are apt to make him even more efficient than younger workers, concludes Giberson.

If the elderly industrial worker is reluctant to change his ways, his reluctance stems mostly from caution. The older employee is apt to be settled in routine with orderly habits. These have created the only world he knows, and he has invested a lifetime in that world. Any sudden change threatens his world and his investment. Most of his trouble on this score is caused by his inability to make a transition from older to newer conditions. Perhaps a transition can be engineered for him, or at least his own made easier. He is haunted by the threat of exclusion, and he feels a discrimination where none exists. He is no longer rich in time and energy, and his knowledge of his own limits sets him apart from younger employees as effectively as his gray hair. He is cautious about new things because he has so little energy to spend; when a new road opens up, he knows that he can only go part of the way and that he may not be around long enough to see any fruit from his efforts. He is apt to feel left behind and unconsidered; such a feeling can, in extreme cases, develop into sickness. The sequence leads to the feelings of being unwanted, barely tolerated, to suspicion of ordinary motives, fancied cruelty and to paranoid retaliation. Furthermore, the elderly industrial worker is jealous of his dignity. When a man works for years at making objects that disappear as soon as made, he has nothing tangible left to indicate his expenditure of energy; his only remaining gauge of success or failure is the attitude shown toward him by his superiors and his fellow workmen. Respect shown him is proof that he has not been a failure. He is quite often deeply bored and unconscious of that fact. He has a hunger for significance, but the symbols about him do not add up into something personally important. Though he would deny this vehemently, his job and his home have become worn and threadbare. He needs a change of pace and an autumn tonic. He has a dread of insecurity, both in the economic sense and in the sense of dependence upon warm human contacts. These feelings are usually accompanied by a rankling sense of unfairness. He is as good as he ever was, yet should he be insubordinate and lose his present job, he would be unable to secure another one. He feels caught in a trap with, possibly, unprotected and meager old age ahead. Retirement, even on pension, will destroy his present life and offer no comparable life in exchange.

These observations of Giberson about the older worker are very impressive. They appear in no such clarity to the worker himself, but, allowing for individual variability, they can be traced as the starting point for many psychiatric cases.

Successful retirement is one of the most difficult achievements of a lifetime, as hard as the climb to the top in business or finance or law. It requires careful thought. Too many persons begin in their 30s and 40s to invest in annuities or to build investments for retirement, but they neglect, until the day their retirement becomes effective, planning what they are going to do with their retirement years. Everybody should allow himself at least ten years, if possible, to develop and test his plan.

Frank,[62] discussing sociological problems in connection with age, stresses the importance of the fact that we are in the process of changing from a large, dependent kind of population to a large, dependent aged population. Statistics indicate, however, that there will be no diminution but a probable increase in the number of people in early and middle adult life constituting the working population; therefore, this increase in dependent aged persons does not mean a reduction in the employable working population. The more serious question is, according to Frank, whether or not we can find a way of using this working group to meet the need for a larger total national income to take care of the dependent aged. A large group of aged persons in our population will have votes and might become a formidable pressure group for pensions of all kinds. The employment of older people encounters some difficulties because of technological changes and the slowness with which the various service activities are being organized. The modern trend in industrial techniques and processes does work against the older worker, and in many factories the decreasing need of skill on automatic machinery, with technical control, likewise depreciates the experience of the older worker. Frank thinks that, owing to changes in the age distribution of our population, the need for a social, industrial, professional and political reform has to be considered, a reform of far-reaching magnitude and significance, few of which we have scarcely begun to recognize, let alone to study.

The essential differences between the modern family system and the preindustrial family have been pointed out also by Tartler.[63] According to Tartler, functions that were formerly attached to the family are now transferred to institutions external to the family, so that they become neutral or even hostile to the family unit. Tasks formerly carried out at home have been taken over by industry and trade. In European metropolitan areas, for example, only 25 per cent of the laundry is done at home, and no laundry facilities are installed in modern, newly built housing blocks. Since the introduction of compulsory school attendance, education, which was formerly obtained at home, is increasingly delegated to public institutions. As the services of social welfare increase, the former benefits of familial solidarity and social security have been taken over by officially organized institutions. Hospitals, old-age homes, social welfare and charitable organizations care for and treat sick and old people. Therapeutic measures can be successfully applied only by experts in special institutions. People now expect to take full advantage of these modern facilities. The aged can't expect any more optimal care and treatment at home.

Because of the modern employment situation, the family is reduced to a unit of two generations. Every family member who does not contribute to the existence of the family by outside employment must become an economic burden to the family. The unemployment of the aged is felt to be an economic burden. The small family, reduced to husband and wife, is no longer considered incomplete.

The function of the aged as testator of the family is becoming increasingly unimportant because old-age pensions are not inheritable.

The tendency to separate the aged from the family is not exclusively or primarily generated by the younger generation. It comes from the old themselves and their desire for independence.

The importance of the grandparents' educational functions is supported mostly by the fact that the parents do not have the time necessary to fulfill this task because of the exacting requirements of modern occupational life.

There is a fundamental difference in the educational situation between the dynamic society of the present and the static society of the preindustrial era. Riesman[64] says that grandparents today serve as examples of how little of real importance one can learn from them. Outmoded are convictions and attitudes of grandparents. Separation between generations occurred as a result of the loss of functions of old people within the family.

Burgess[65,66] finds Tartler's ideas too pessimistic and feels that the social world for the aged is not a retreat but an opportunity. The new relation of parents and adult children needs to be based on the recognition that each generation has his own life to lead. The older generation should give up the expectation that its chief interest in life is to be preoccupied with the affairs of their children. The younger generation should realize that in living their own lives, there still remains an area of common interest with their parents.

One study found that living independently but relatively

near each other seemed to be the optimum situation for the majority of cases.

In a special study of my own,[67] the conflicts between the generations (generation gap) have been described in the following way:

> In our culture, the family typically consists of three generations—children, parents and grandparents. Many studies have shown that each of these age groups (generations) has its own purpose, goals and values. And yet, for the sake of the emotional health of each member and the existence of the total culture, they must share in at least one value—the conservation of the family itself. This must be done in such a way that the esteem and respect of each member is maintained and the process of self-growth is emphasized.

Conflict between the generations will arise and can lead to intense feelings of ambivalence and hostility and can actually destroy the harmony of the family, temporarily or permanently. This inevitably will lead to much emotional upset of all family members and, therefore, of culture itself.

Psychoanalytic theory and experience has much to say about these processes. For one thing, we must consider the roles each generation in the family should play for maximum mental health and stability. The children's normal role is one of dependence in regard to physical, economic, social, intellectual and emotional development. The key dependency relationship is that of consistent and continuous love among all family members. Without it, the child will grow up confused, insecure and emotionally disturbed. The parent of the same sex is needed to supply the identification figure. The Oedipus complex has to be worked through. The path from dependence to independence is frequently blocked with obstacles which must be reversed or overcome. This is always done with the parents or parental symbols serving, consciously or unconsciously, to the child, as his model. The child must be helped by the family to grow toward adult independence. If not, the child will remain fixed in the early phase of psychosexual development or will regress backward toward immaturity under stress.

In contrast, the way of life of the adult is characterized by the attainment of the maximum level of independence. Maturity is closely related to independence and can be defined as follows: (1) the constructive drives will be greater than the destructive ones (Karl Menninger);[68] (2) the mature adult will be capable of overcoming a wide range of frustrations and stress without being deeply disturbed; (3) adjustment will be good within family life, the chosen field of life work, and in the many facets of community living; (4) the individual will reach the highest level of psychosexual development with libido directed toward the heterosexual partner (Freud).[69]

In all of this, the role of the grandparents is not clearly defined. We need much research in this critical area, since the older person has his own problems, liabilities and assets which cause conflict or strength in the family unit.

Streib and Thompson[70] suggest two reasons for disturbed relationships between the younger and older generations. These are (1) friction over the rearing of children and (2) differences over the perception of the aging process itself, with the older generation having more overt and clearer recognition of aging. Frequently, the sheer contrast in health and vigor among the three generations reinforces the older person's awareness of aging.

Davis[71] pointed out that a certain amount of friction between generations is a universal phenomenon. He described three variables, found in most cultures, that tend to produce conflict between parents and children: (1) the age or birth-cycle differential between parent and child; (2) the decelerating rate of socialization with advanced age; and (3) the intrinsic differences between young and old on the physiologic, psycho-social and sociologic planes.

An interesting study was done by Yarrow and associates[72] on social psychological characteristics of old age. These investigators emphasize that the aged family is not as familiar in research as the young family and that data and concepts derived from research on the latter cannot be directly transferred to the former.

According to these authors, data are especially needed in

regard to the following problems: What roles does the aged individual take with his peers and with younger adults? How, in concrete form, does the older person attempt to control others, to maintain his independence? What is the interplay between the psychological and the mechanical aspects of behavior, such as the older person's more limited locomotion, restrictions placed on him in the use of a car, visual and auditory dysfunctions? We clearly need data as well as the methodology.

Considering some of these liabilities of the older generation, it is understandable why family conflicts between adult children and elderly parents are unavoidable. Misunderstandings, resentments and hostilities on both sides can be frequent. Because of the many physical sicknesses connected with aging, some oldsters request continuous treatment and care which might test the patience of the younger generation and, eventually, bring the family into economic distress.

Self-pity and hypochondriacal complaints of the elderly can become difficult to tolerate, according to Busse.[73] The retired and financially dependent parent often is felt to be a burdensome responsibility. A distorted image of aging and concern about dying and death might disturb younger members of the family. A hopeless outlook for the future and life in general by the emotionally sick elderly person can cause hostility and depression in the insecure and ambitious young person. If these negative aspects of old age play a predominant role, the elderly person will be pushed aside by the younger generation, will become isolated, and will be considered an intolerable responsibility. We can thus see how the elderly parent can be institutionalized when he does not need it—and then forgotten by the young generation after a certain length of time in the institution.

Under these circumstances, rationalization will be used to justify such action by the younger generations to make themselves feel less guilty. Lack of housing facilities is frequently given as an excuse. Occasionally, the tendency of some of the older people to get disengaged can be abused. The process of disengagement from society, according to my experience, is not as frequent or as egosyntonic in the elderly as stated in the literature.[74] I found that it is often imposed upon the older generation by rejecting family members or by society and made to seem to be the real attitude of the elderly. Although elderly people need more time for rest and can't participate in many of the sportive, recreative and social activities of the younger generation, most elderly people feel ambivalent about their loneliness and reach out for contact with young people, especially of their own family.

There is some truth to the observation that elderly individuals frequently feel the necessity to be "left alone," that they become less social-minded and more interested in their own emotional, spiritual and intellectual life, and that they frequently consume considerable time in thinking of their bodily ailments. However, they almost invariably feel ambivalent about their solitude. They realize that many activities of young people are undesirable for them and out of their domain. The majority of elderly citizens have less interest in the parties, dances, sports, technical interests, economical-political problems and nightly amusements of importance for the younger generation. They are aware that they are in need of more sleep, of greater periods of rest and relaxation than younger people. They nonetheless resent being excluded from the younger generation's plans and interests on very many occasions, to be left more or less completely to their own devices. Although older persons withdraw at times voluntarily from many attitudes, customs and activities of younger people, they so frequently do so with resentment and disappointment and stay in lonesome, unhappy seclusion. Their wish to encounter younger people "half way" and to find some common goal and interest has often been rejected. A great number of elderly citizens do not want to intrude into the life of younger people due to their lack of understanding of the needs of the other generations and also because of their lack of understanding of the needs of the other generations and also because of their fear of feeling unwanted. Many old people sometimes desperately reach out to meet younger people but without success because of misunderstanding and lack of empathy on both sides.

According to Kastenbaum,[75] the basic problem for the aging individual is how to find meaning and satisfaction in life as he becomes increasingly less able to keep everything going at once. He can select one or several "parts" for sustained involvement; he can try to preserve the "whole" at the expense of the "parts," or he can vacillate between these solutions.

Havighurst,[76,77] in extensive studies, pointed out that the relationships between levels of activity and life situation are influenced also by personality type, particularly by the extent to which the individual remains able to integrate emotional and rational elements of the personality. Of the three dimensions on which we have data—activity, satisfaction and personality—personality seems to be the pivotal dimension in describing patterns of aging and in predicting relationships between level of activity and life satisfaction. It is for this reason, also, that neither the activity nor the disengagement theory is satisfactory, since neither deals, except peripherally, with the issue of personality differences.

Brehm,[78] too, has given the problem of retirement much thought and came to the conclusion that for the aged retired person to satisfactorily adjust to his new circumstances, he must find an acceptable set of values for older age as a basis for a new self-concept and new roles through which he can express his new self-image—that is, the opportunity to interact with others in his new circumstances. There is a problem of a basis for a new self-image equal in respect to the lost one. Unless the aged individual can in some way retain the self-image of an employed person by at least a partial work involvement, he cannot find a solution with an equivalent amount of respect (Cavan).[79]

Videbeck and Know[80] approached the study of alternative patterns of participation in aging and found they were identical to those of younger active persons.

According to my own experience, elderly people should never be completely isolated. Frequent visits with younger adults, especially with children, are necessary and desirable and should be encouraged. All three generations give to each other something of great importance. The life experience—the patience, greater sympathy, wisdom and understanding—of very many old folks should be utilized by the less mature and still growing generations to their own benefit and progress.

To have children and grandchildren near is not only an aid to overcome old people's loneliness, but it very often symbolizes older people's goals in life. In their relations with grandchildren or children, parents and grandparents are frequently reminded of their youth. They feel themselves reborn in their children and would like to help them in many ways. They try to educate, to advise, to protect, to lead, and they find in these duties a fulfillment of their own life. Youngsters help them to play, to relax, not to take things so seriously, to laugh again, to remain young in spirit and to understand the problems of the younger generation. Older people indeed become less rigid, less stiff and seclusive, and appear happier when contact with younger persons is maintained. However, the playfulness of the youngster must not become a burden and a stress. Children and grandchildren should realize that older people frequently like to be alone, tire more easily, need more sleep and rest, occasionally even in the daytime, and they do not wish to be burdened with too great responsibilities for others any longer. At times, older people like the quietness of meditation and thought, often to prepare themselves for the life after death. Being aware that life may soon end for them, they need time to accept this idea and must struggle to overcome their fears. Only when they have worked through these feelings and are free from resentment and regret are they able to continue to live happily. However, when elderly persons see hostile competition from the younger generation, who wants the oldsters out of the way as quickly as possible, then the relationship between the older and the younger generation becomes disturbed and hate is engendered. Therefore, tact on both sides will be necessary. Younger people should respect older people's feelings and try to understand their handicaps, their sicknesses, their inability to be playful, to take certain responsibilities and to plan a life in the future.

On the other hand, youngsters should be prepared to accept

from the older generation what they alone can give them—the fruits of a life experience, patience in reaching out for an individual's goal in life, making careful and consistent plans, work and relaxation, thoughts about how not to lose themselves in unnecessary, superfluous and harmful vices, and striving to recognize the true values of life, how to obtain and hold real friendships, to make matrimony and family life more harmonious and rich of fulfillment and to accept the individual's own handicaps and shortcomings without complaints and resentments. Only at a higher degree of maturity, which comes with age, can we realize that wrong done to others in our lives has only harmed ourselves and, being free from many unconscious strivings, hate subsides, and love toward others grows and develops. Especially when our sexual drive and erotic feelings toward the other sex become less urgent, many stress situations in life can be avoided, and our energy then becomes free for many hidden and undeveloped creative powers. Therefore, old age can have certain definite advantages which younger people are unable to obtain.

Another important factor, which I would like to emphasize on this occasion, is the advantage of having a mixed group of both sexes living together in a geriatric unit. The author has observed that many geriatric patients released from hospitalization after twenty or more years have great difficulty adjusting on the outside in nursing homes, foster homes or in their own families because of previous lack of contact with persons of the opposite sex. Women remain afraid of men and men of women when they have not conversed together for many years, when they have never had picnics, dances or other relaxation together. Even sitting at the same table with persons of the opposite sex becomes a problem after many years of isolation. Erotic feelings, suppressed or repressed for a long period of time without outlet of any kind might break through and induce the patients to become upset, disturbed and may even be responsible for a relapse into a psychotic state. Life in a hospital has to be as natural as possible and a substitute, to a certain degree, for home life. Rooms with plenty of space, air, sunshine, nice curtains on the windows, attractive pictures on the walls, and the mingling of elderly persons of both sexes in the dining room, during occupational and recreational activities and especially in group psychotherapy have definitely great therapeutic value. Geriatric patients, as the author could prove, not only adjust more easily and better when the sexes are mingled in a psychiatric hospital, but for them the step of leaving the hospital and starting a new life in a nonhospital environment, is less stressful with fewer readmissions to the hospital.

Bortz,[81] in a recent paper, states that the family rather than the individual should be recognized as the basic unit of society. This is self-evident, for the illness of one member of a family group, young or old, has an impact on all the rest. Frequently, the older the individual, the greater the threat to the vitality and security of the family.

Discussing the approach to the geriatric patient, Kobrynski[82] emphasizes the necessity of a new approach. In the past, in the approach to an elderly patient, physicians and the general public suffered from a defeatist attitude which sometimes bordered on neglect. Today there is clear evidence that elderly patients can benefit greatly from modern restorative therapy, the use of which is gradually becoming an essential part of medicine. The physicians, in addition to providing health service to individual patients, have a responsibility to stimulate the development of community resources for the aged and to raise standards in institutions.

Orientation of therapists and nursing staff in the biological, psychological and social aspects of aging is necessary.

Kutner[83] describes the issues raised by the aging population as affecting social and economic life in five areas: (1) maintenance of the continuity of community life for the aged; (2) abolishment of age discrimination in employment; (3) preservation of an income adequate for decent living; (4) wide-ranging reforms in institutional living arrangements; and (5) prevention of factors alienating the elderly from the rest of society.

The second factor of very great influence on the emotional and physical health of our aged, is our cultural attitude toward

them. Our century is the "century of youth." We are all directed toward social and economic goals, are driven by an irresist-
able force to achieve them. We live in a world of continuous
competition and therefore we have to work compulsively and
strenuously to improve our social position and maintain it. We
live in continuous anxiety. We decide that "time is money."
We are overburdened with work, have no time for recreation,
for relaxation, and, sometimes, not even for sleep. We lose the
connection with the beauty of the natural world and with the
rhythm of life. Music, art, literature, for us, are considered
a "waste of time." We fail to find relaxation in our family life.
Emotionally detached sexuality frequently has taken the place
of love, and the responsibilities of our family life make us
worry day and night. We sometimes lose the feeling of being human and do things mechanically and without interest. Then, as
the end of our life comes nearer to us, we are exhausted and have
the feeling we have not really lived at all. In such a world of
tension, of compulsion, of work and of competition, elderly people are considered a burden. They know it, they feel it, they
see and hear it and are unhappy and dejected. Elderly people
can't compete with this modern trend any more, and they are
unable to change it. We, however, can and should do something about it.

Especially appropriate in this connection is Linden's[84] paper,
"Relationship Between Social Attitude Toward Aging and the
Delinquencies of Youth." He points out the connection between
our lack of respect toward the elderly person and indeed our
attitudes of rejection, intolerance, impatience, hostility and an-
noyance with the elderly parents or grandparents and the increase of juvenile delinquency. Children who can't identify with
father or grandfather, who consider elderly parents useless and
burdensome, who laugh about Senior Citizens, and who grow
up without parental support and without ethical judgments are
frequently in a state of rebellion. A culture where life experience and wisdom are held in no esteem, where parents and
grandparents are not felt to be examples of goodness and personal worthiness, and where authority is rebelled against be-

cause it is not considered important must create simultaneously an atmosphere of freedom without limits, of wanting without boundaries, and of egocentricity. When the child does not learn to look upon the elderly as an object of respect, then the door is open for rebellion and disobedience. Police control can never substitute for parental support. Punitive measures will never be as effective as the parents' love and understanding. Linden concludes that our own cultural attitude is therefore partially to blame for the increasing delinquency of our children.

The third factor to consider is the feeling of economic insecurity from which so many old folks suffer. Old people have to live protected from the most urgent needs of our daily life. Public welfare helps, we know, when need arises, but this help should be given willingly and effectively so as not to cause an emotional blow and severe loss of self-esteem. Special housing projects, hospitals for the chronically sick, rehabilitation and recreation centers have to be built. Only in this way can we prevent many emotional and physical sicknesses of elderly persons. The accent should, however, never be on welfare but on rehabilitation. Most elderly persons can still do useful and meaningful work if they find understanding for their problems. They might work more slowly and finish a task far later than a young person would, but they are often able to work with great exactness. In Switzerland, for instance, many watchmakers are older people because of their greater experience and patience. In the United States, to a limited degree we are using the skill of elderly persons as furmakers, tailors and even as machinists. There are many examples of great contributions by the elderly in politics, in art, in philosophy and in science. The achievements of Michelangelo, Churchill, Gandhi, Toscanini, Einstein, Albert Schweitzer and "Grandma" Moses immediately come to mind. These are people who, in spite of their old age, have been able to create things of which all humanity is very proud. We do not need to take a pessimistic attitude in regard to elderly persons. They do not have to regress, to deteriorate, to become useless, or to be considered superfluous. They can offer something younger persons do not possess: wisdom, patience and life experience which should and can be utilized for the benefit of all of us.

III

THE PSYCHOLOGICAL ASPECT

THE EMOTIONAL NEEDS of the elderly people have been described lately by a number of outstanding physicians and psychiatrists. It has been stated that the cause of many of the mental breakdowns in later life can be found in experiences dating from childhood and adolescence. We know that these early experiences play an important part in the origin of schizophrenia and manic-depressive psychosis. Now we recognize that mental disturbances like involutional psychosis and senile dementia also have their roots in childhood experiences.

In a well-known paper published in 1948, Gitelson[85] has given importance to the emotional aspect of aging. This author attributes six different patterns of adjustment to old age: (1) a decreased memory for recent events—a turning away from the painfulness of the present; (2) a sharpening of memory for the past, especially for time when life was successful; (3) a more self-assertive attitude as compensation for insecurity; (4) a mild depression caused by isolation and the feeling of loneliness; (5) introversion and increased sensitivity with querulous and paranoid attitudes; (6) a free floating anxiety caused by death among the same age group, especially when relatives are involved.

The irritability of older psychotics often has its source in the inability to cope with the environment as well as in physical decline. Apathy in elderly persons can be considered as an outcome of the detachment of the individual from painful memories and events of his life. Kaplan[86] states that one of the effects of losing friends and relatives is to give the older person not only a feeling of being alone in the world but also a feeling that, without social ties, he is unprotected and insecure. Of a somewhat different opinion is Overholzer,[87] who suggests that our attitude of overprotection of our old people results in personality change and that we should be careful not to accelerate, in older people, their entrance into a condition of dependent helplessness. Loss of independent activity frequently produces an emotional crisis. Retirement, for instance, gives more opportunity for introspection, for self-evaluation, for the development of delusional ideas and for regrets. Older men, who tend to be more seclusive and withdrawn than older women, are more inclined to cerebral arteriosclerosis, while women suffer more from senile dementia.

The problem of becoming aware of being old has been studied by Jones[88] and others. Subjects have been asked how and when they noticed for the first time they were growing old. Jones found that in most cases the following symptoms were mentioned by his patients: (1) breakdown of the locomotor apparatus; (2) difficulties of a nervous kind; (3) sense-organ impairment; (4) deterioration of the skin and the hair; (5) increased tendency to fatigue; (6) greater need for short periods of sleep interposed during the day.

Kuhlen[89] points out that the biological changes accompanying old age have been extensively studied in themselves but have not yet received the attention they deserve from the point of view in which they are perceived by the individual. Such changes imply much more psychologically than a diminution of actual functional capacity only. Greying hair or increased girth can become quite threatening, and losses in strength, sensory acuity, sexual capacity and energy level may represent losses in ability to achieve gratifications in accustomed ways. Special threats to the aging person appear to be developments which reduce mobility and restrict the individual's freedom to make constructive adjustments to frustrating situations: lack of advancement in position, increased responsibilities to a growing family and biases against employment of older individuals. According to Havighurst,[90,91] an adequate Ego function is not only dependent upon freedom from physical disease or crippling but also involves the element of hope. Everyone will be able to endure pain and hardships if there is hope that the suffering eventually will come to an end and the future will be brighter. The child gives up many of his gratifications for responsible achievement because each step brings approval and love from his parents. Indeed, approval and love from others and the individual's yearning for them is an important factor in a healthy Ego function. Hope for a better future, love and approval from others often is lacking for old folks, and their life is empty because of lack of interest of friends, neighbors and relatives. Therefore, it is extremely difficult for them to maintain a good emotional equilibrium.

It is well known that paranoid trends become more evident in senile persons, especially if their personality traits have always been of a suspicious kind. Old people often feel unwanted, and this realization may be conducive to delusional ideas. Frequently, the content of the delusions centers around the idea of being robbed, of being poverty stricken or of being poisoned. The tendency to commit suicide increases with the higher age group. The loss of loved ones or physical sickness with a poor prognosis may precipitate this tendency and always must be given careful consideration. Criminal offenses generally decrease with old age, but sexual offenses, fraud, violation of the narcotic laws, arson and poisoning frequently bring older people to court and, afterwards, to mental institutions.

Studies of the emotional needs of the elderly have been made by comparing their attitude with the attitude of the child. The child has been found to be a fundamentally dependent person getting acquainted with independence, which appears desirable but full of danger. The child makes progressive efforts toward mastery of his helplessness. The aged person, on the other hand, has gone through this state of independence, but his self-sufficiency has become seriously threatened by decreasing effectiveness and by the progressive breakdown of his defenses. The child emerges from isolation and helplessness and renounces his private strivings to please society or the family. The older person likes to participate in everything belonging to society, but society shows a hostile and rejecting attitude towards him. The child has unlimited energy, great ambition and psychic elasticity which helps to keep him from being hurt, and he reaches out for the future. The aged person finds his supply of energy diminishing. He fears the future, is blind to reality and finds himself in a continuous state of disillusionment. He no longer believes in a world of love and peace and loses interest in accomplishment.

Meerloo[92] describes one of the first symptoms of the elderly emotionally disturbed patient as the spontaneous return of emotions repressed in childhood, giving evidence of a breakdown of mental defenses. In several types of climacteric neurosis increased aggression became evident. For instance the climacteric or postclimacteric woman, frigid before her menopause, now tries to attain sexual satisfaction, liberated from responsibility and fear of childbirth. She is hastening for complete gratification before she dies, showing a phobic acting out of what has been repressed for many years. In my experience, such behavior causes anxiety neuroses of a severe degree and often leads to divorce and domestic problems. Especially when the conscience is strong, the anxiety increases accordingly and gives evidence of a severe internal conflict. Furthermore, with diminishing Ego control in advanced age, aggressive impulses might break through, leading to self-destruction or to destruction of family relationships.

Often these drives become more evident and less controlled by the use of alcohol or drugs. Increased sensitivity to environmental influences is observed. Change in environment, retirement from business, lowered income, or forced moving and replacement by younger people with loss of prestige might precipitate a mental disturbance. The aged person cannot accept the reality of being mortal, and in his dreams secret plans for immortality play an important role. The fear of insomnia, according to Meerloo, represents the dread of loneliness and death. Some old people bury themselves in squalor and refuse any contact with the outside world; others hoard money and possessions and live in constant fear of losing them. Old age might therefore be considered a traumatic neurosis with continuing trauma.

With the increasing emphasis on body function, the elderly person grows more and more narcissistic and stingy. For the geriatric patient, the diminishing of his heart function means, symbolically, loss of love and should be well understood as a psychosomatic reaction.

Goldfarb,[93,94,95] in his long experience with treating geriatric patients, describes that many of these patients appear to be outwardly depressed but are more self-aggrandizing than self-depreciating. Although feelings of failure and frustration are expressed, the environment is usually blamed and attacked, frequently in a paranoid fashion. These patients reveal little evidence of guilt, but fear of retaliation is usually present. They do not seriously contemplate or attempt suicide although they may make such gestures. Although they often express a wish to die, to go soon, or to have it over with, they protest lack of courage or give moral and social reasons for their self-restraint from suicide. Outstanding is the complaint of joylessness, lack of pleasure, feelings of futility and hopelessness. For them, eating, sleeping, personal relations, work, hobbies and entertainments are not pleasurably anticipated, presently enjoyed or happily reviewed. Therefore, Goldfarb believes that in geriatric patients the absence of true depression is related to a decreased capacity for affectionate relationships. They fear most of all the loss of the material implications of personal relationships: the personal care, protection and dominance over those from whom they derive care. They are unable to retain the friendship of persons who can afford protection and are concerned about desertion and abandonment. The joylessness with the sense of futility and hopelessness is a means of obtaining and guaranteeing care. Old folks want pity, compassion and care from parental surrogates and frequently do not permit themselves pleasure. They often prefer to feel persecuted and deprived. At times such a facade of helplessness and hopelessness masks a persistent attitude of hopeful expectancy.

Gerty[96] considers that the appearance of many mental breakdowns during the aging period may be caused by a collapse of the personality under stress and emphasizes as etiologic factors conditions other than organic disease. Some of these personality disorders are due to a continuation from the preinvolutional period and represent psychotic regressions and manic-depressive and schizophrenic reactions. Others show psychoneurotic regressive tendencies. The same author believes that the pathological condition producing a picture of mental symptomatology in old people may not be primarily in the brain. Even aphasia may result from impaired brain circulation, resulting from a combination of cardiac disease and narrowed cerebral vessels. Organic factors, involving the whole organism and not the brain alone, and emotional factors, taking into consideration the premorbid personality and the individual reaction to a stress situation, appear to be of greatest importance.

Masserman[97] points out that, in regard to the dynamics of aging, it is important to differentiate between the actual disabilities of aging—i.e. the diminished capacity to perceive, differentiate, abstract and evaluate the environment and respond in a properly versatile and efficient fashion—and the reaction of the individual to such impairments. The essential dynamics of the aged depend on the attempts of the individual to compensate for his declined powers and status. Similarly, as the paranoid grandiosity of the paretic is not caused by the disease itself, the aged person tries strenuously to reassure himself of his physical competence from bedroom to golf course. He builds and defends philosophic and mystic systems promising some form of immortality. Finally, he tries desperately, and sometimes pathetically, to retain or reestablish what human relationships he can salvage here on earth.

Busse[98,99] is of the opinion that guilt is apparently an unimportant dynamic force in the psychic functioning of so-called normal elderly persons and is seldom conducive to depressive features seen frequently in geriatric patients. According to Busse, the older person is no longer living in a highly competitive situation which mobilizes hostility and aggressive impulses that end in self-condemnation. This lack of competition with others, however, appears to foster the development of inferiority feelings which form the basis for depressive episodes.

The aged person cannot counteract inferiority feelings by demonstrating his superiority through competition. The source of the inferiority feelings is primarily an inability to fulfill needs and drives and is accompanied by doubts which develop when the oldster is reminded of the decreasing efficiency of his bodily functions. Therefore, biological, sociological and psychological alterations have to be taken into consideration in relation to the origin of depressions in geriatric patients.

Schiele[100] stresses the importance of decline in strength and the loss of physical attractiveness of old people. Social and economic limitations and infirmities impose handicaps on the older age group. The loss of good looks or physical prowess frequently represents a severe blow to self-esteem. In addition to these defects, reduced visceral function, diminution in the various senses (particularly of sight and hearing), reduced sexual function, failing memory and increased lability of emotions become a reality. These are enough reasons why an elderly person might feel restless, unhappy, unwanted and rejected. Low reserves and loss of flexibility make the elderly person more vulnerable to physical and psychological stress. As he cannot deal effectively either with the future or the present, he tends to overvalue the past. This is one of the reasons why neurotic complaints among the aged are common. However, the types of disorders that occur depend largely on the personality organization.

Very old people (100 years or older) in relatively good health have been examined in regard to those stress situations in an experimental setting.[101] The results reveal that persons who live to be very old have been able to avoid frustrations and to escape conflicts with authority. They ascribe special value to independence and attempt to apply the principles of democracy as a basis for cooperative and productive living. They worked hard and long hours but were not anxious to get to the top and therefore did not suffer from hypertension. They have a social character, a sense of humor and are well liked. They do not worry about things beyond their control and are disinclined to argue. They try to avoid tension, daily annoyances and frustrations that produce chronic stress, leading to homeostatic disequilibrium. They are honest with themselves and face sickness and frustrations squarely and objectively without fear and therefore remain healthier and succumb less to acute sicknesses. They are able to stand catastrophe in their family life and do not react too severely to personal injury. They are not easily "shocked."

Liebman[102] gives importance to the fact that marriage does not present a special problem for "potential centenarians." They enjoy marriage, have a low record for divorce, have relatively many children and eventually marry again in their 90s if the spouse dies. The problem of fertility cannot force them into a stress situation. Death does not arouse fear and desperation in them but is considered as a natural consequence of life itself. Religion for them is important and helps them to overcome their fear of death. Hobbies, interest in recreational activities and friendly interpersonal relationships are used to avoid the feeling of being lonesome and isolated. The "potential centenarian" is rarely in a hurry and dislikes working under pressure. In his casual, quiet way he is able to work long hours without feeling rushed, and therefore he does not suffer easily from circulatory damage. He is able to interrupt his work for a brief rest, a walk, or for recreational activities. Abuse of drugs, coffee or alcohol is avoided. The "potential centenarian" is seldom to be considered an "accident prone" person, seeking relief from tension and anger by impulsive actions and unconscious suicidal attempts. He is able to think before he acts and therefore he is in less danger of getting hurt emotionally.

Only by maintenance of physical and emotional homeostasis have many artistic, literary and scientific achievements been made possible at advanced age. Michelangelo completed the dome of St. Peter's at 70; Sophocles wrote *Oedipus Tyrannus* at 80; Goethe, past 80, completed Faust; Gladstone became Prime Minister at 84; and Handel, Haydn and Verdi created immortal melodies after the age of 70. Creative powers, genial ideas and artistic greatness are not bound to any age but seem mainly to be an affair of willpower, workability, endurance, enthusiasm and homeostasis.

Grotjahn[103] believes that growing old is often felt as narcissistic trauma, for it represents and repeats a castration threat. The neuroses of old age are defenses against castration anxiety. Old infantile wishes do not die; nor do they fade away; they are waiting to return. There are three different potential reactions for the elderly to the existential problem of aging. The first is the normal solution: it aims at the integration and acceptance of a life as it has been lived. Then there is increased conservatism and rigidity of the Ego, trying to hold the line of defenses according to the pattern of previous neurotic adjustment. The third possibility is frank neurotic or frequently psychotic regression.

Kaufmann,[104] discussing the analytic treatment of depressions in old age, describes the inverted Oedipus complex occurring in such instances. Aged and dependent individuals may regard adult offspring much as they formerly regarded their own parents. Considerable ambivalence takes place when the patient, who once helped his child in growing up and was the authority figure, now has to take orders from his children.

According to Simon,[105] prevention of mental illness in older people depends in large part upon the provision of good health services throughout life, but especially in middle age and the later years, and of various supportive services for the elderly that may mitigate the effects of the social, economic, physical and psychological stresses to which old people are subjected.

For the first two-thirds of life, the Ego is concerned primarily with mastery of the outer environment; in the later years it is increasingly concerned with the self. In the 50s, introspection increases, focusing especially on one's accomplishments or the lack of them.

Berezin,[106] in his excellent book on *Geriatric Psychiatry*, emphasizes that loss in the aged includes, in addition to persons, such variables as job, status and money; bodily functions and abilities, such as vision, hearing, skin elasticity, sexual drive and locomotion; independence and self-respect. Other organ systems of the body may be affected, for instance, impaired cardiac function or intellectual capacities, such as memory. These are losses idiosyncratic to aging and not encountered in early life. The reaction of any individual is, however, unique for him by reason of his previous level of libidinal organization, system of defenses and adaptations, and general personality structure.

Butler,[107] who studied human development in the aged extensively, stresses that the mirror image experience appears to be an excellent method of acquiring data about self-image and body-image. Personality factors, organic impairment and bodily changes contributed to reactions before the mirror which ranged from shame and rejection of the image to anxiety and to unabashed pleasure (narcissism). Drawings of the self (with and without the mirror) suggested that one facet of the self-view included sometimes bizarre bodily dissolution. Maintenance of a sense of inner identity in the context of internal and external changes seemed critical to successful adaptation.

According to Deutsch,[108] the climaterium is psychologically a traumatic experience to every woman. It marks the end of her femininity. Menopause comes as a narcissistic injury. With the onset of this period, which goes hand-in-hand with a regression in physiological functioning, there may be a heightening, perhaps as compensation, of libido activity. There is a displaced reaching out for new love objects. The woman who, up to now, had perhaps been well adjusted, begins to try to act "young again." She may become dissatisfied with her husband and even attempt flirtations or affairs with younger men. This period can readily be recognized as the so-called dangerous age. There begins a phase of "retrogression," a regression to abandoned infantile libidinal drives. The genitals become depreciated as an organ. According to Deutsch, "it is now too late." There are two climacteric phases, both repetitions of the phases of puberty in reversed order. In the first phase of attempted compensation, the libido is strongly directed towards the object, with a strong narcissistic longing to be loved. In the second phase, there is a devaluation of the genital, renewed masturbation of the clitoris, turning away from reality and reversed Oedipus phantasies.

The function of reproduction and the loss of direct object relationships are the center of conflict in the aging woman.

During the corresponding age period in the male, the focus of conflict also centers around the sexual problem. The principal difference, however, between males and females in old age, is in the field of sublimations. Some observations show that the intensity of aggression which the reactionary old man displays towards youth depends in part on how revolutionary his own attitude had been during puberty.

One important aspect of the problem of maturity is the question of the rigidity of the Ego. With increasing age the majority of people tend to become fixed in their opinions and reactions; they lack elasticity. The youthful radical matures into the older conservative. This is due, partially, to a more objective evaluation of reality factors with increasing age, but childhood conflicts appear to be present and are of overwhelming importance dynamically even in old age. According to studies of Kaufman and others, the neuroses and psychoses of this period are definitely of a pregenital type, for example, the involution melancholia with regression to orality. Instead of the anxieties dying out or being dissipated with the period of the climacterium, they actually become more threatening and, in the face of "actual" conflicts, which cannot be solved, the individual regresses more to psychotic reactions. According to statistics, emotional disturbances appearing for the first time in later life are more likely due to psychosis than to neurosis.

The sexual expression in late life has been studied extensively by Weinberg.[109] It is a fact, according to Weinberg, that no one seems to want to touch the older person and that very few seek physical contact with them. Therefore, the psychobiological hunger of the elderly remains ungratified, and frequently regressive maneuvers related to dynamic formulations of oral, anal and phallic preoccupation take place. Chronological age, according to Weinberg, is no barrier to the continuation of sexual life in the older person.

Denber[110] is of the opinion that in many women in advanced years, sexual adjustment will follow the pattern of previous adjustment. If neurosis was a way of life in younger years, sex will be used to prevent the real problems from coming into awareness. Sometimes the awareness of personal failure, coupled with ongoing physical failure, can precipitate a severe depression.

Verwoerdt, Pfeiffer and Wang[111] made a longitudinal study at Duke University from 1954 to 1969 in regard to sexual behavior in senescence and came to the conclusion that age and the degree of sexual activity are not related in a strict linear fashion. The incidence of sexual activity declined from a level of more than 50 per cent during the 60s to a level of 10 per cent to 20 per cent after age 80. The degree of sexual interest was more intimately related to aging than activity. Strong degrees of interest did not occur beyond age 75. However, the interest in sex did not show any age-related decline; mild to moderate degrees of interest tended to persist into the 80s. Marital status had little effect on the activity and interest of the aging men, unmarried women had a negligible amount of sexual intercourse, but about 20 per cent of the subjects did report sexual interest. The sexual activity and interest of men was greater than that of women, according to these investigators.

Hamilton[112] expresses the opinion that sexual frustrations, so often observed in older persons, are related to somatic and environmental handicaps carried over from early life. Elderly individuals regress frequently to the autoerotic and pregenital satisfactions of infancy. Masturbation and eroticism (the latter related eventually to intestinal difficulties) are common in the elderly age group. The Ego strength diminishes and the strivings of the Id are suppressed with more difficulty.

Other interesting observations with geriatric patients have been made by Schilder.[113] This author believes that the apprehension and fears of the presenium and early senium are overcome by deterioration. These patients may feel happy and strong again, revive heterosexual wishes, or may at least feel gratified by oral satisfaction. The fear of being poor, of being robbed or of being persecuted may persist and may act as a constant stimulus of escape into a state of greater happiness. The aging and the senile may even try to get renewed satisfaction in the sexual approach to younger people. However, in the majority of cases, this approach to youth will remain in the realm of daydreaming, phantasy and confabulation. There are indications that these regressions follow the pathways through which the individual has gone in childhood, adolescence and adult life. There are psychic compensations in senility. When the individual is no longer capable of enriching or maintaining his relations to the outward world, he regresses to infantile situations and looks from there to new possibilities. The geriatric patient has a definite relation to time and space, though the objective facts of time and space are distorted. Even when the senile regresses, he does it differently than the schizophrenic. He cannot go back to a magic world but remains in a world which fulfills the strivings and desires of his adolescence and manhood.

In regard to intellectual decline in elderly persons, Bowman[114] describes the correlation existing between the physical and mental condition of the patient. Memories seem to get progressively worse from about 30 years onward, caused eventually by atrophy of the brain. However, memory loss can be partially caused also by loss of interest and lessened intensity of feeling in the old person. Learning ability decreases with age because learning of new things requires breaking down long-established patterns, a difficult procedure for elderly individuals. Older persons sometimes feel, as their life span grows short, that there is no need for new experiences and therefore they do not try to learn. Reasoning ability and perception of spatial relations decline with advancing age. Elderly persons can hardly deal with unfamiliar material. Imagination, judgment and wisdom might be affected to a variable degree. While many older persons have good judgment and reveal wisdom in their actions and are therefore welcome in councils of government and on the bench, others show considerable decrease of their intellectual functions and are unsuitable for such positions.

Ebaugh[115] stresses the factor of fear in old age. The old person is plagued by fear of physical infirmity, loss of economical security, approaching death, indifference of children, loss of friends and social contacts, loss of capacity of sexual gratification and, above all, by the fear of useless loneliness. Frequently the family members of aging persons react to these fears with resentment: they are afraid of restriction of their own freedom, of caring for an invalid who can easily become a neurotic tyrant and can hardly control their own resentment against the elderly. The family increases the problems of the old person and eventually disrupts family life. Oldsters might also touch off anxiety in others, because hidden fears of sickness, death and disintegration are lurking in everyone. In this way even greater rejection of the unstable adult takes place.

In my own clinical experience, periods of very active intellectual attention are followed by such signs of emotional fatigue as confusion, lack of orientation, poor organization in discussion, and a tendency to talk too much or to change the subject frequently. Emotional blocking with retardation of thought, movement and emotions might become evident when the brain is exhausted, a fact due perhaps to inadequate oxygen supply to the brain. A period of rest after a time of intellectual fatigue and continuous tension is therefore not only indicated, but necessary to restore the brain again to normal functioning.

We have to be aware of the fact that an emotional attitude might be connected with physical disease. Old folks with digestive disturbances, especially those suffering from a peptic ulcer, might be moody and occasionally bad tempered. Diabetic patients reveal a more or less evident emotional instability, owing to continuous anxiety and fear of dying suddenly. Cardiac patients are generally known to be very restless, demanding and tense. In a very interesting study, Dovenmuehle and Verwoerdt[116] have described certain relationships between length and severity of cardiac illness, the frequency of hospitalization and a depressive response. A mild cardiac condition, according to those investigators, does not differ from a severe one in terms of its potential to provoke serious depressive symptoms within the first three years of sickness. Frequent hospitalizations, even in mild cardiac illness, are accompanied by moderate and severe depressive reactions. Perhaps depressive symptoms contribute to frequent hospitalizations, especially with mild grades of cardiac illness; a hospitalization itself is an important factor in producing a depressive symptom. These investigators found that almost two-thirds of hospitalized patients with cardiac disease had significant depressive symptoms. Patients suffering from general and cerebral arteriosclerosis, when consciously or unconsciously aware of their handicaps, might also become deeply depressed. It is known that elderly persons might not only suffer from one but from several physical handicaps and can be in a continuous state of anxiety and tension due to the realization of their physical sickness. Prostate troubles are often the cause of elderly men feeling invalided and rejected. It is a fact that an old person can hardly be in perfect health; sickness, however, even chronic sickness, does not need to be considered hopeless and impossible of recovery.

Chronic sickness might stimulate the defense mechanism of our body, developing a tolerance against pain and imbalance. Our potential faculties of repair and compensation are great and can be utilized for recovery. Sickness can be followed by convalescence, the most powerful force of regeneration in human life, and recuperation from sickness can be a great emotional experience by strengthening our failing powers of immunity and active self-defense. Our vital forces could be stimulated, and the accent should never be on custodial care but on rehabilitation. Even old people with serious chronic sickness can become useful and remain very active members of their profession and of society.

By the mechanism of compensation, physical handicaps might even become the cause and beginning of great creative powers, as has been proven many times. Everything depends on the individual's personality, on his emotional attitude to physical handicaps, on his optimism and his willpower. There is no reason, I am convinced, for elderly persons to react with the loss of their emotional equilibrium to some of the inevitable physical sicknesses associated with aging. Instead of revealing signs of intellectual decline and emotional regression, they can remain mature, self-reliant, independent, and feel happy and satisfied by reorientation of their goal in life and by stimulation

of their creative powers. Aging should not evoke punitive, re-
strictive, uncompromising authority, but the elderly person can
and should—by his warmth, his humanism, his experience, his
orientation around group principles—be the leader of our community and, as Linden expresses it, "consultant in living."

Guilt feelings and a great deal of anxiety in geriatric patients are due, in my observations, to the sexual strivings
condemned by both the individual and by the environment.
Sexual strivings and excesses might become, in old age, a source
of physical sickness, because the associated excitement may contribute to circulatory disturbances and their consequences. Generally, the erotic feelings of elderly persons are directed toward
younger persons, even children, and may show themselves in
attempted rape or exhibitionism; more often, however, they are
sublimated and appear only in the form of normal, natural affection of the aged for children and represent an effort to regain
their lost youth by identification.

Malamud[117] reports studies of the personality organization
in psychiatric disturbances of geriatric patients and comes to
the conclusion that for overconscientious, rigid and sensitive
personalities, adjustment in later life becomes more difficult. The
same author holds the following responsible for emotional disturbances in old age: failure to provide old folks with special
interests, failure to satisfy their needs in later years, sudden loss
of beloved objects (husband, wife, children, the home, etc.),
operations or injuries of organs generally related to reproduction
(pelvic and breast operations, prostatectomies, etc.) and loss of
social and economic security.

The intellectual changes in old people were studied especially by Miles[118] at Stanford University. He found that imagination seems to be ageless and that verbal associations, interpretations of meaning, and recognition of relationships show less
tendency to decline with age than do speed, organization, recall
of unfamiliar material and difficult logical procedures. The total
intelligence quotient scores show a progressive decline with
advancing age. Wechsler[119] points out that the curves show a

parallelism between loss of brain weight and decline of ability with age.

Gilbert[120] has done well-controlled studies about psychometry of the aged and aging and concludes that probably the best way of attacking the problem of mental decline with advancing years would be to follow through life a large number of individuals and subject them to various tests at intervals from childhood to senility. At present, however, this method is not suited to our needs, as we have no records of early mental tests of our older individuals and yet are faced with the practical problem of determining their maintenance or decline of mental ability. In spite of certain admitted inadequacies of our present tests, psychometry can even now render definite information on both the mental ability and the mental deteriorization of older persons.

First, however, we must state definitely to what age group we refer, when we speak of mental decline with advancing years. To plot a curve of mental decline, we must have norms at least for each decade of adult life. To measure groups of individuals between the ages of 40 and 70 covers too wide an age range. Our prime concern must be with individuals over the age of 60.

According to Gilbert, there are two ways of measuring mental deterioration in the aged: (1) by the use of general intelligence tests and (2) by the use of a test which will control the original intellectual level of the individual.

The use of general intelligence tests to measure the mental ability of old people has two faults. While speed plays an important part in the practical consideration of the efficient functioning of an individual, it does not tell us anything about his intellectual level and often serves to obscure his real, native ability. To measure general intelligence in adulthood, the tests should be standardized for each decade, for only thus can we compare the abilities of an older person with the general intelligence of his contemporaries.

The second important fault in the use of intelligence tests on older people is the failure to take into consideration the original intellectual level of the individual being tested. We may find that a group of old people score at the average or below the average of a group of young people on certain tests, but this does not indicate whether or not any individual in this group has suffered a decline in mental ability. No numerical rating on a general intelligence test can tell us this, even if the test be standardized for each decade as mentioned above. For example, an individual who scores above the average may actually be deteriorated in that he does so poorly compared with what he once could do. We must first know his original level of intellect before we can say he has or has not deteriorated mentally. The attempts to control this by means of educational and occupational levels are obviously unsatisfactory because of the different opportunities, both educationally and vocationally, which have come with the passing years.

The Babcock Test of mental efficiency, a test first designed for the measurement of mental deterioration in psychotic persons, is an instrument which controls the original intellectual level of the individual. For this reason, this test is satisfactory for use with older people. This test is based on the assumption that deterioration occurs first in new learning and in the formation of new associations and last in earliest formed material.

It does not mean deterioration of general intelligence but rather deterioration of one phase of intelligence—the efficiency phase which, after all, is the functioning side which must interest us practically if we are working with older people. The factor of speed has to be taken into consideration. Although speed is not used to gauge the intellect of an individual, speed is a factor of practical importance. For example, what good would it do for an individual to know the correct responses to make in driving an automobile if in a crisis he could not make these responses quickly enough to avoid a collision?

The use of vocabulary as the control of orginal intellectual level will undoubtedly draw adverse comment, but investigators do agree that vocabulary shows marked resistance to age. Rather unexpectedly, it seems to depend relatively little upon the amount of formal education. For example, Gilbert found in persons in the 60s a number of individuals who, without a day of formal schooling in their lives, scored higher on the vocabulary test than did some of his young college graduates. A good vocabulary seems to be a thing which natively superior persons acquire, regardless of educational advantages or the lack of them, and something which natively inferior persons cannot acquire, regardless of opportunity. On the other hand, vocabulary does not increase materially after school years. Gilbert's studies support this conclusion. Of special interest in this connection is the close similarity of vocabularies of parents and adult offspring, even when not living together. By this method, then, we can make a true comparison of older and younger persons of matched intellect and also compare an individual's efficiency with that of his normal contemporaries of like intellect. This is a practical point to consider, particularly in connection with employment possibilities of older people.

Using this method, there is a definite decrease in efficiency for all levels of intellect in the 60s, the loss being greatest on tests involving learning and the formation of new associations, flexibility of perceiving relations, retention and motor ability and least on tests such as the giving of opposites, general information and simple repetitions. Taking the group as a whole, the percentage of loss varies from 57 per cent loss in the learning of paired associates to 12 per cent loss in the giving of general information. The average loss is 29 per cent. Speed is an important factor on most of the tests and, when not weighted for time, the percentage of loss of the older group decreases but is still decidedly significant and remains greatest in the type of test which requires the formation of new associations and least in tests closer to simple vocabulary. There is a marked learning defect. There is very little overlapping in the efficiency indices of the older and younger groups with evidence also of a progressive deterioration within the decade of life from 60 to 69 years inclusive. Another interesting point is a marked tendency for the very highest levels of intellect to show relatively less decrease of efficiency than those of lesser intellect, raising the question of whether it may not be that the greater the intellect with which one is endowed, the less he tends to deteriorate or the longer he tends to retain his original equipment of efficiency.

Individual differences in mental deterioration are great, and these are of practical importance to anyone working with older persons. Both physical condition and temperament are important considerations. Likewise, employment seems to keep up efficiency, although at times it is difficult to determine whether some of the unemployed are unemployed because they are inefficient or whether deterioration has progressed more rapidly because of the condition of unemployment.

Gilbert concludes that, although there are some in the 60s who are fit only for retirement or old-age pensions, there are others who are capable of (and would be much happier) functioning at a decreased pace with remuneration scaled to output of work. There are others, particularly in the higher types of work, who are capable of producing at great value to society. It is not profitable to discard all aging individuals, regardless of individual ability or desire. We must not forget that the older person has fewer industrial accidents, spoils less material and causes less turnover than the younger person, thus, to some extent, offsetting his disadvantages of less speed and decreased adaptability. Also, the experience and knowledge he has gained in his own field with the passing years are not to be turned aside lightly.

In a review regarding the psychology of aging, Granick,[121] comes to the conclusion that, in old people, the overall intelligence test performance shows a marked and progressive decline in relation to increase in age.

It appears that on subtests regarding vocabulary, general information and reasoning problems, in which speed is not a factor, older adults have an achievement comparable to younger subjects. Memory functioning, efficiency of performance and tasks involving the relinquishing of old habits, however, are found to be difficult for old people. Furthermore, projective tests reveal senescence to be associated with a decline in personality functioning in such important areas as flexibility and control and social adaptability. Generally, however, the evidence would seem to indicate that for the average person, old age does not mean increased emotional instability despite the new problems of adjustment they encounter.

Birren[122] made special studies regarding changes in sensation, perception and learning and observed that with advancing age there is an increased latency in all voluntary responses. The older organism seems to require additional time to integrate or perceive information from the environment and to "program" the appropriate response. Longer response latencies appear to have their greatest consequence in complex or serial tasks. The inference is drawn that the capacity of the central nervous system to integrate complex activity is limited. However, the high redundancy inherent in our verbal and social skills tends to mask the appearance of age changes in the central nervous system. According to Birren, generalizing should be avoided.

IV
A NEW CONCEPTUALIZATION OF
THE GERIATRIC PATIENT

ACCORDING TO MY OWN experience over more than fifteen years of intensive clinical studies with geriatric patients, the psychodynamics involving especially the elderly's attitude toward death and dying, their distorted "image," and their lack of a goal in life have not been sufficiently explored yet and are conducive to "a new conceptualization of the geriatric patient."

With the exception of a few authors, the actual thought content of the geriatric patient has received little research or theoretical attention, especially in regard to attitudes toward death and fear of dying, whether on a conscious or unconscious level. Rose[123] states that, generally, death is welcomed only by those who are suffering great physical or mental pain or by those who have reached such a condition of lassitude that one nothingness seems to be an inconsequential substitute for another. It is noteworthy that even in those individuals described by Rose the fear of death is so great that they experience great ambivalence and conflict over such desire. Even when the older person reconciles himself to dying, the actual fear of dying hangs over his thoughts and expectations for the future.

Wahl[124] notes the dearth in psychiatric and psychoanalytic literature of any real description or systematic treatment of the fear of death. Such fears clearly are not clinical rarities. According to Wahl, it is very important to study the fear of death and the predominantly magical defenses which are set up against it. Defenses of concealment or displacement consume energy which must be drawn from other sources, causing impairments to living in an unhampered, free and creative way.

Meerloo[125] implies that fear of death follows the Oepidus

period. He describes it as the symbolic product of the fear of castration which derives from improper resolution of the Oedipus complex.

Feifel[126] explains that death can mean different things to different people, depending on the nature of the individual's development and his cultural context: (1) death represents a lesson of transcendental truth incomprehensible during life; (2) death is a friend who brings an end to pain through peaceful sleep; (3) it is a means of vengeance to force others to give the deceased more affection than they were willing to give him in his life; (4) death is escape from an unbearable situation to a new life without any of the difficulties of our present life; (5) it is a final narcissistic perfection, granting lasting and unchallenged importance to the individual; and (6) a means of punishment and atonement (a gratification of masochistic tendencies).

Hutschnecker[127] explored the personality factors in dying patients and describes the handling of death in terms of the person's lifelong pattern of adjustment. The person who desired in his life to be nurtured by others is likely to see death as the return to mother earth: the symbolic substitute for an earlier symbiotic existence in the womb. The person who in his life sought conquest may wish to die as a hero so that others and he himself should not perceive him as a failure. According to Hutschnecker, the physician, who is sensitive to the dynamics of dying, cannot help but relate these processes to the defenses and problem-solving technique used by the dying person in his day-to-day living. It is my own observation that persons who have difficulties in handling their daily problems and stresses will also have the same type of difficulties in handling the problem of dying. On the other hand, those who have been able to balance their lives by integrating primitive instincts with moral, religious and other demands can, as a rule, accept and handle their own dying in a mature manner.

Wolff[128] points out that restlessness and insomnia in the elderly frequently are caused by the fear of dying. This behavior frequently increases at night. Wolff,[129] in another paper, relates the patients' attitudes to death to the underlying personality structure. These attitudes are related to lifelong patterns and defense of passive-dependency, schizoid, compulsive, paranoid and other personality features which characterized the person's life style.

PERSONALITY TYPES

The attitudes of six groups of geriatric patients toward aging and death were studied. There were fifteen subjects in each of the following psychiatric groups: passive-dependent personality, schizoid personality, inadequate personality, emotionally unstable personality, compulsive personality, and paranoid personality. Assignment to the diagnostic group was made by psychological testing and psychiatric evaluation and diagnosis of the entire life adjustment. All ninety patients were in good contact at the time of the study. Seventy were males; twenty were females.

Personality Type and Reaction Toward Aging and Death

Passive-Dependent Personalities

This group showed the following attitudes in depth interviews and in lifelong behavior patterns: Becoming old frequently caused them to become depressed, disturbed or agitated. They tended to lean upon others and felt great concern over the death of a spouse or their nearest relatives. They acted like helpless children, abandoned and dejected when a spouse died or when a brother or sister on whom they relied was hospitalized for a long period of time. It was interesting to notice that these patients also showed decreased resistance against infections (common cold, for instance). Their will to live and endure seemed to be diminished. None of the patients belonging to this personality type, however, showed special concern about dying; they regarded death as something unavoidable and as a relief from painful events.

Schizoid Personalities

These patients were shy, withdrawn, seclusive and mistrustful. They did not like taking part in activities and preferred to remain aloof. They had difficulties in meeting people and mingling with others. They did not show much anxiety when the problem of death was discussed with them. Involvement in any kind of emotion, in social activities, or in plays with other patients and even visits of relatives were considered bothersome and to be avoided. Movies, theater plays or television performances had no special attraction for them. They preferred to stay "disengaged" and did not want to take part in the social life of the psychiatric ward because they feared being hurt. Sometimes these patients became completely mute because they were afraid of life. It was difficult to evaluate with exactness their feelings toward becoming old or toward death because they never really had felt dynamic, outgoing, social-minded or active. In a sodium amytal interview, two of them showed suspicion, mistrust, uncertainty and a moderate amount of fear when problems of old age and dying were mentioned.

Inadequate Personalities

This type showed feelings of inferiority and insecurity in work, marriage and life. Aging was considered by them to be an additional handicap. They worried a lot about their daily tasks, resigned easily, lost patience, changed jobs frequently and could not defend themselves well in a stress situation. Many times they complained about physical symptoms (headaches and stomach trouble, for instance). The life patterns frequently showed their attempts to avoid stressful situations and responsibilities and to shy away from competition. Aging made them feel more inadequate. They suffered a great deal of anxiety because of memory defects, feelings of fatigue and decrease of concentration ability in connection with their age. Sicknesses like cataract, glaucoma, decreased hearing or heart conditions accentuated their inadequacy and were considered by them as "catastrophes." All of them suffered from great fear of death and dying and they were generally depressed. Most of these patients revealed great reluctance to discuss old age or death.

Emotionally Unstable Personalities

These patients suffered frequently from crying spells, and they were easily upset and excited. They were oversensitive, resentful and unable to stand frustrations. They felt rejected easily and were inclined to depressions. When appreciation was shown to them, they became euphoric and eventually hypomanic. They were greatly concerned with their own bodies and with physical sicknesses and were in need of continuous support. The problem of death was considered a great threat, inducing emotional outbursts of agitation and depression. They revealed a great desire for stability, dependency and security and resented anything which might threaten these needs.

Compulsive Personalities

These patients were particularly disturbed over their aging. For them, all work had to be done with perfection. They were concerned with all the small details in their life and worked strenuously toward a certain goal. They liked to compete with other persons and tried to do everything better. Even small mistakes were not tolerated, and when things went wrong by mistake, they felt guilty. Their severe Superego guided them through all their life. They were unable to relax and enjoy life. They had to be considered "anal characters," sublimating their hostility by compulsive attitudes. Getting old or dying was rarely taken into consideration by them on a conscious level; sicknesses were denied and minimized. When these compulsive characters realized that they were getting older, they suffered from a "catastrophical reaction." They took a tragic viewpoint of dying, struggling desperately to stay young and efficient. As they became older, they made a great effort to do their daily duties as perfectly as before, worked harder and more strenuously and did not permit themselves leisure time or relaxation. They usually became increasingly rigid. When memory defects appeared, they tried to overcome these by following a daily schedule and a strict routine. Any change in this routine was felt as a disaster, causing irritability and agitation. Death was considered a very great threat. The members of this group feared the unknown and had great difficulty accepting death as a reality over which they had no control.

Paranoid Personalities

These people suffered especially when difficulty of hearing or decreased eyesight played a major role in their lives. They frequently imagined they were neglected or were considered a burden and superfluous and became suspicious of other people. Often, delusions of persecution appeared and they believed their friends, relatives or neighbors were enemies who wanted to "get rid" of them and who would eventually bring them to a psychiatric hospital for the rest of their lives. They had phantasies of "hell" or "heaven" and were in continuous turmoil. Occasionally, the religious paranoid personalities believed they were messengers sent by God to fight against the devil and prophesied the "end of the world." They became interested in cranky habits, became food addicts or became involved in miracle cures for evidently incurable sicknesses or became political fanatics.

Paranoid personalities were divided into two groups. Six of them wished for and welcomed death as a liberation from "togetherness" with hostile people on this earth, feeling that only after death could they have peace. They considered life as a burden not worth retaining. This group thought that some of their physical illnesses were sent by God as punishment for imaginary sins. The handicaps and disabilities of old age were felt to be a special burden, and death, consequently, was considered a welcome relief. The other nine members of this group were very much afraid of death and clung to life desperately because they were suspicious of what would happen to them after death. They suffered from extreme restlessness and insomia and were especially concerned about being left alone in the dark. Their agitation increased tremendously at night.

Further studies led me to review my work with geriatric

patients in psychiatric institutions and to try to determine the frequency and nature of death fears. How serious is the fear of death and dying for the geriatric patient? Are other attitudes also involved? I have kept detailed notes of my depth interviews as well as individual and group psychotherapy sessions over the past sixteen years with geriatric patients hospitalized in different psychiatric institutions. Data were obtained from forty patients through depth interviews and from three hundred others through individual and group psychotherapy sessions.

PATIENTS' CHARACTERISTICS

The average age of the 340 patients was 64 years. Forty were female. None had severe memory defects or suffered from great difficulty in concentration. Included were those with delusions and hallucinations as long as they had some contact with reality and could coherently express their ideas concerning death and dying. Agitated, hostile and depressed patients were also included. Thirty-eight per cent showed primary chronic brain syndrome associated with cerebral arteriosclerosis, senility, chronic alcoholism or luetic infection. Sixty-two per cent showed a schizophrenic reaction.

Thought Content

1. In 80 per cent of all these patients, the problem of death and concern about dying played a most important part in their emotions. One-fifth of these patients denied, in the beginning, that they were concerned with these problems, but they openly admitted in later interviews or therapy sessions that they frequently were afraid to fall asleep or to be alone in their room because "something might happen to them" or they "might not wake up any more." The majority of these patients liked to keep the light on at night as late as possible and frequently called the night nurse in order to get attention for minor physical ailments. More than half of these patients were unable to sleep at all without sedatives or tranquilizing medication at bedtime. Their dreams frequently centered around "falling into water"

or "swimming in a lake" (return to the uterus). It is interesting that practically all patients who showed very little death concern, even in depth interviews and daily living, were diagnosed as schizophrenic reaction. In these patients anxiety of any sort was much decreased due to their emotional bluntness.

2. Many elderly persons have a disturbed image of aging and try everything possible to remain young. They identify with youth in behavior, clothing and manners, frequently in a bizarre or artificial way. Some never fully accept their own aging as a natural process; nor do they learn to live with it. They consider it a severe trauma. They are afraid of losing their physical attractiveness, their strength and their potency. Cataracts or glaucoma and hearing difficulties may frighten them. Many consider only the negative factors of old age and fail to see the positive ones. Positive aspects of aging center around the elderly person's greater understanding of life, his patience, his experience and wisdom. These permit successful emotional equilibrium. For this purpose, the image of aging has to be changed among aged persons themselves. Braceland[130] particularly emphasizes this. Karl Menninger[131] says "hope" in the aging is an important dynamic factor for successful adjustment.

3. Finally, very characteristic of the elderly person is his regard for his goal in life. Many have lost their goal or purpose in life. If the person's profession or occupation represented such a goal, forced retirement is felt as a tremendous blow. When artistic or scientific goals cannot be fulfilled because of physical incapacities, the elderly person is particularly prone to break down medically and emotionally. When the goal in life has been marriage and a close family life, death or absence of near relatives frequently leads to depression and agitation.

The elderly person needs somebody to live for, something to be deeply interested in, something to permit him happiness and fulfillment. Life has to remain meaningful and purposeful. If the goal of life is lost, he becomes emotionally sick and is more prone to physical complaints. This important factor of life goal therefore deserves special consideration in any emotional rehabilitation program for a geriatric patient. The importance of a "meaning" of life has been described extensively by Frankl.[132] According to this author, we can discover the meaning of life in three different ways: (1) by doing a deed; (2) by experiencing a value; and (3) by suffering. This idea, I believe, is of greatest significance especially for the geriatric patient.

PART TWO

V

SCREENING PRIOR TO ADMISSION
TO A PSYCHIATRIC INSTITUTION

APPLICATIONS FOR ADMISSION of geriatric patients to a psychiatric institution are becoming more and more frequent. Many state mental hospitals are overcrowded with patients, and the number of elderly patients asking for hospitalization increases yearly. They are brought to the hospital at times already committed by a court order. The hospital physician not admitting these would be exposed to punishment by law for not obeying a court order and not admitting a patient even though he disagrees with the commitment order and believes that commitment to a psychiatric institution with consequent loss of civil rights of the patient is not necessary.

More often, however, patients are brought to the psychiatric hospital on a voluntary basis, or, in some states, for a ninety-day observation and treatment period. In many such cases, patients could be evaluated on an outpatient basis by a competent psychiatrist and treated as outpatients, so that hospitalization might be avoided.

When a patient is brought to the mental institution for a ninety-day observation and treatment period, this amount of time can be significantly shortened if the psychiatric staff is convinced that only a few days of hospitalization are needed for the evaluation of the patient and that the patient can be treated without hospitalization.

Some superintendents of overcrowded state mental institutions are well aware that there are a great number of geriatric patients admitted for hospitalization who do not need it. The psychiatrist examining the papers at the time of admission—or prior to it—finds sometimes that the mental condition of the patient has been described as confused, threatening or delusional and that the diagnosis of schizophrenic reaction has been given without sufficient substantiation. On the first and subsequent psychiatric examination at the psychiatric hospital, the diagnosis of the family physician cannot be confirmed. The question should immediately be asked as to why the patient had been found in need of urgent hospitalization. Does he really need to be hospitalized at all?

For this reason, I found it necessary to reexamine applications of geriatric patients to a state mental hospital and have done a study on 105 elderly patients. The results were very revealing. There was clearly an exaggeration of the patient's symptoms given as the reason for application for admittance to the mental hospital. The most frequent reasons for the urgent recommendation for admission to a mental institution were found to be the following: (1) lack of adequate training and understanding of the family physician who found himself unable to treat a disturbed and occasionally confused elderly patient; (2) lack of empathy and patience on the part of the family who considered, consciously or unconsciously, the geriatric patient as a burden and found it difficult to take time or make an effort to supervise him or give sufficient emotional support; especially, members of the younger generation—children and grandchildren—lacked understanding of the oldster's problems and this eventually led to apprehension about things "going to happen to the grandchildren"; (3) denial of community support and neighborly help in some cases because it was thought to be too troublesome or not indicated; (4) the belief that the easiest way out of the situation was hospitalization of the patient in the nearest psychiatric institution where he would get adequate treatment or supervision; (5) the still common attitude among physicians and laymen in the United States that emotional disturbances are rarely curable and need to be treated in a closed psychiatric facility; and, finally, (6) the desperate economic condition of the elderly individual who may not have sufficient means to pay for a long period of psychiatric treatment. Often such people live alone and are left to their own devices without anyone else's care, having to cook, shop and clean for themselves and tend feebly and apathetically to their own daily hygienic needs.

Many years of experience and study in psychiatric institutions have convinced me that many patients of the elderly age group were not originally in need of hospitalization and that others have been kept in such a hospital for many years after their remission from a psychotic episode. A great number of geriatric patients have received maximum hospital benefits and could be released from the psychiatric hospital. Others were actually returned to their families or put in foster or nursing homes to the surprise of other members of the patient's family or the community who had "forgotten" the patient or lost interest, believing that rehabilitation in community or family life was not possible. Recently such a patient, even after twenty-eight years of hospitalization, was released from hospitalization and adjusted himself well in the community. The release of this 64-year-old former lawyer from hospitalization, having been diagnosed as a "burned-out schizophrenic" created great resistance on the part of the patient's brother and guardian, who did not "believe" in such an improvement in the patient and who was definitely afraid to be responsible for him.

It is quite possible that this situation might vary in different geographic areas and on different socioeconomic levels. Goldfarb[133] made an extensive study in several homes for the aged and in nursing homes in New York City and concluded that four out of five of all such aged persons in the nonhospital institutions surveyed were problems in management or were disturbing elements. At least one-third of them, according to psychiatric evaluation, would be eligible for admission to a state hospital by present standards should a complaint or petition for such care be made. This demonstrates, according to Goldfarb, that the old-age homes and nursing homes in the New York metropolitan area are acting as reservoirs of aged mentally disturbed persons and thus slow the flow of patients into mental hospitals. The state hospitals in New York tend to receive persons who are qualitatively more antisocial and disruptive, or confused, unmanageable and in need of terminal nursing and medical care.

There is no reason to doubt Goldfarb's findings and evaluations. It indicates only that the situation in New York City in regard to admission for hospitalization and psychiatric treatment in a psychiatric institution is different than in other states. First of all, it appears that the number of elderly persons with emotional disturbances is actually greater in relation to beds available in the state mental hospitals in New York City than in less urbanized areas. I also suspect that the economic conditions, including the housing conditions, in the greatest metropolitan area in the United States play a definite role in the placement and management of emotionally disturbed patients having problems of adjustment.

On the other hand, in more agricultural states where the housing problem is a minor factor and the economic condition seems to be more stabilized, other factors appear to be of greater importance.

A study of 105 geriatric patients, male and female, was undertaken in a state institution of the State of Kansas in 1957 and lasted more than a year. The study was started in September 1957 and ended August 1958. Of the twenty-eight patients carefully examined during the first five-month period, only seven were admitted to the hospital after careful examination at the Outpatient Department. These patients were either psychotic or suicidal or showed signs of a rather severe behavioral reaction and were found in need of hospitalization. Seven patients were sent to nursing homes for further care. The remaining fourteen were returned to their families with special treatment recommendations to the family and the general practitioner who treated them before the referral to the hospital by court order for a ninety-day observation period. They were admitted to the hospital but discharged the same day after careful evaluation by the psychiatric social worker and a nurse.[134]

By August 1958, all 105 geriatric patients were evaluated on this outpatient basis. Of this number fifty were hospitalized (47%), twenty-four were sent to nursing homes (23%) and thirty-one were returned to their own family (30%). The patients sent to nursing homes belonged predominantly to the group of chronic brain syndromes, associated with cerebral arteriosclerosis and combined with physical handicaps, in need of care and treatment which could not be given at home. Those who returned to their home environment were behavioral problems of a minor degree, with occasional confusion, memory impairment, restlessness or reactive depression but without signs of psychosis. They were treated by their family physician with tranquilizing medication or energizers under advice of the psychiatrist. In many cases of this kind, misunderstanding or wrong attitudes of other members of the family appeared to result in the precipitating stress producing these emotional disturbances.

A case history will best illustrate these observations and the correct procedure employed in this study.

> The patient was a 75-year-old, married, male janitor who was accompanied to the hospital by his wife and daughter. The social history revealed that the patient, during the past two years, frequently became angry and fought with his wife. He also wandered away from home and got lost. When found by the police, he could not understand why everyone was so excited and interested in his whereabouts. He had been treated by his family physician with tranquilizers. His wife was 51 years of age. This was the second marriage for both, having lasted eleven years to that time.

> The patient came to our hospital because of a ninety-day observation court order. At the interview he was friendly, cooperative and answered questions willingly. He was neatly and cleanly dressed and was apparently used to taking good care of his personal appearance. His intellectual faculties were poor, however. He was not oriented to time or place and had a severe memory defect for recent and remote events. He believed himself to be 57 years old. He did not remember what he had eaten the day before. Although he had a fifth-grade education, he did not know how to multiply 9 times 9 and could not name the capital of his state. In his lifetime he never had a hobby of any kind except for participating in church activities. When asked to explain his wandering, he answered that he "just had to go" and did not know why. He liked to walk through the country, but he would always return. "I never want to go too far," he said. His thought processes were neither slow nor fast, and his thought content was not delusional. Hallucinations were not detected. Two months previous

to the interview he started working as a janitor every night and seemed to like his job. He had quit his job seven weeks later because of his confusion and wandering away and getting lost. He did not have insight into his condition and did not reveal any signs of anxiety. He denied worrying about money or anything else. When asked about his relationship with his wife, he answered, "I love my wife and I get along with her very fine."

Physical examination: Blood pressure was 180/90. There was a systolic murmur heard over the base of the heart that was not transmitted. The second aortic sound was accentuated and there were premature ventricular contractions. There was a cataract on the right eye and the left eye had had a cataract removed surgically. The neurological examination was normal. There were no other significant physical findings.

After the interview with the patient, the wife and the daughter, together with the social worker, were called into the office of the psychiatrist. The wife expressed disappointment in the marriage because she expected her husband to take care of her. This he had been able to do for the first few years until he grew older and less physically fit, so that he was gradually less able to continue satsifying her material needs. Bills for their new car and household items mounted until she had to go to work the preceding year in order to meet the expenses. Her work kept her away from home during the day, and his work kept him busy at night. These circumstances appeared to be the reason why the patient, who was left alone most of the day, became upset and wandered away from home. The psychiatrist explained that this situation had to be changed. The wife should stay at home more often than formerly and should give her husband more loving care in order to eliminate his feeling of loneliness and rejection. Otherwise the patient might become considerably more disturbed in the future. With these recommendations and the prescription of a tranquilizer for ten days, the couple was sent home. A follow-up study of this patient after six months showed that he was well adjusted at home and not in need of further psychiatric help.

It has to be pointed out that follow-ups were necessary and had to be done on a monthly, three-month, or six-month basis. Four of the 105 geriatric patients belonging to an average age of 65 years continued to return once weekly to outpatient treatment for group or individual psychotherapy regularly from three to six months. The patients transferred to nursing homes were carefully supervised by visits to the nursing homes by the social worker who was called when the patients got upset, disturbed, depressed or showed any kind of management problem. Conferences between the nursing home administrators and the psychiatrist were frequent and eventually done through telephonic communication. Psychopharmacological drugs were given after contacting the general practitioner visiting the nursing homes. Occasionally a visit by the psychiatrist was found necessary for better observation of the patient in the nursing home or in the circle of his family and was done with the consent and common accord of the treating family physician. Such a communication system has been found of great importance and makes the treatment of the geriatric patient outside the hospital much easier. In addition, training courses in geriatric psychiatry were given at the hospital under the supervision of the psychiatrist, with the help of all the members of the psychiatric team. These training courses, given about every four months at the hospital for about ten nursing home administrators, definitely helped toward a better understanding of the geriatric patient's behavior and attitudes in the nursing home. Conferences and seminars were given on psychiatric problems of the elderly patient which soon awoke the interest of many general practitioners who came to observe and to learn.

It was remarkable that during the same period of time (from September 1957 to August 1958), fourteen other applications for admission to the psychiatric institution were withdrawn by the family when appointments were given to evaluate the patient prior to admission. The reason for this withdrawal of the applications probably was the fact that hospitalization was not believed so urgently needed.

These are the observations of an eleven-month study at a Middle West state institution in which overcrowding had been a tremendous problem previously. In this case we saw that the probate judges showed understanding and willingness to cooperate with the state institutions and the state government for a better treatment of the elderly citizen. I believe that the situation is similar in many other states and that careful prehospitalization evaluation of geriatric patients and treatment on an outpatient basis, combined with direct transfer of a certain number of patients to supervised and licensed nursing homes might be of definite value for the welfare of the elderly patient as well as for the community.

The results of my study therefore permit the following conclusions:

1. Definite admission procedures to psychiatric institutions should be deferred until after a ninety-day observation and treatment period.

2. Evaluation by a psychiatric team prior to admission of the geriatric patient is necessary and of value.

3. Treatment on an outpatient basis for geriatric patients with emotional problems should be given when indicated.

4. Better rapport between the hospital psychiatrist and the family physician referring the patient for hospitalization is needed.

5. Nursing home administrators should receive training at the psychiatric hospital in order to be able to understand and handle more efficiently the problems of the aged.

6. The services of all community resources such as senior citizens clubs, day centers and volunteer organizations should be optimally utilized.

7. The psychiatric team should gain a good picture of the economic condition as well as the emotional background of the family environment of the patient prior to the requested hospitalization.

8. Rapport and frequent communications between the hospital's psychiatric team and the staffs of the nursing or old age homes are vital.

In recent years, a special research study has been made by Epstein and Simon[134] at the Langley Porter Neuropsychiatric Institution in San Francisco in regard to screening of geriatric patients. These well-known gerontologists confirm my findings in regard to the importance of screening of the geriatric patient and report that there are no grounds for a philosophy of therapeutic nihilism with elderly patients admitted to a psychiatric screening ward. About one in four is not diagnosed as suffering from a chronic brain syndrome. The prognosis for return to the community for patients suffering from a psychogenic illness is excellent. Patients with acute brain syndrome tend either to die shortly after admission or to recover from their acute brain syndromes and are returned to the community. Where the acute brain syndrome is combined with a chronic brain syndrome, the patient who recovers from this tends to return to the community unless the severity of the chronic brain syndrome is such as to require prolonged hospitalization. It is evident that treatment prescribed for these patients must include intense, comprehensive medical and psychiatric care. Signs of depression, paranoia and confusion may disappear. Alcoholic patients with confusion may clear within a short time. Although two-thirds of the total sample admitted to the screening ward were transferred within a week to a state mental hospital, such disposition can be avoided if suitable alternative facilities can be provided. Finally, over 90 per cent of patients formerly committed to state hospitals now may be placed in other facilities.

PART THREE

VI

THE TREATMENT OF
THE EMOTIONALLY DISTURBED
GERIATRIC PATIENT

TREATMENT OF THE CONFUSED GERIATRIC PATIENT

AT THE PRESENT TIME about 38 per cent of all patients in V.A. and state mental institutions are in the elderly age group—60 years old and upwards. This percentage is increasing due to the fact that a great number of schizophrenic patients, admitted twenty or more years before, remains hospitalized. Many of these show signs of confusion.

The primary causes of confusion are histological and pathological changes of the brain substance itself. Clinically, confusion is considered one of the cardinal signs of the brain syndrome, acute or chronic, usually caused by cerebral arteriosclerosis or senile brain alterations. Confused patients frequently talk in an incoherent way. Outside the hospital they wander around, get lost on the street, enter other people's homes by mistake, take a bus or train in the wrong direction and are in danger of traffic accidents. Inside an institution, they feel "lost," "mixed up," cannot find their ward or their room and occasionally are in a state of severe agitation. Confused patients might also suffer from other symptoms of brain damage; they are not oriented to time, place and person, their memory is defective for recent events, or their intellectual faculties are decreased. At times they are emotionally unstable, irritable and impulsive, lose their temper and threaten other people. Often they show lack of common sense and judgment by throwing money away, buying useless things or hoarding material they cannot use. Their thought content is disconnected and their talk occasionally does not make any sense. Patients of this kind are treated in increasing numbers by the general practitioner who usually prescribes a tranquilizing drug and recommends close supervision at home. If this therapeutic approach fails, the family physician refers the patient to a psychiatric institution. Because of the importance of proper treatment for these patients suffering from confusion in consequence of a brain syndrome, psychiatrists and gerontologists have conducted studies and experiments to find a rationale to improve their condition. Some methods have shown satisfactory results.

Use of Metrazol®

Metrazol (pentylenetetrazol), in oral form, combined with nicotinic acid or without it, has been tried for a number of years. The recommended dosage is 0.1 gm, four times daily. An extensive study has been done by Smigel, Serhus and Barmak[135] involving twenty patients. These authors report that in ten of eleven disoriented patients, disorientation disappeared completely. Four confused patients became rational. All twenty patients showed a marked drop of systolic and diastolic pressure. No side effects were observed.

Seidel, Silver and Nagel[136] treated twenty-three patients with Metrazol in combination with nicotinamide (400 mg daily) for a period of ten months. The age of these patients ranged from 62 to 89 years. Of these twenty-three patients studied, fifteen showed moderate to good results. Improvement in regard to intellect and memory was reported. These authors considered the treatment with Metrazol and nicotinamide a step forward in the halting of degenerative processes.

Levy[137] has found in a special experiment involving twenty-nine patients treated with Metrazol that all his patients (on psychological examination with the Wechsler-Bellevue Intelligence Test) achieved an average gain of six points in the intelligence quotient. According to Levy, this was probably due to an increase of attention. The patients were able to concentrate better on the tests and took more interest in them.

This author found Metrazol of value for elderly patients suffering from mild memory defects, confusion and deterioration in the absence of more serious emotional and psychiatric disturbances. It appeared especially helpful in combating symptoms of abnormal behavior and personality changes.

Fong[138] studied the usefulness of Metrazol on thirty-five patients of the geriatric age group for a period of 180 days. The average dosage was 0.2 gm, four times daily. A higher dosage than that, according to Fong, caused mild nausea and vomiting. The majority of these patients were diagnosed psychosis with cerebral arteriosclerosis. Of the thirty-five patients, sixteen showed improvement. A decrease in anxiety, agitation, emotional lability, irritability and fatigue was noted. Better sleep habits and general physical improvement were achieved.

Linden, Courtney and Howland[139] made a controlled study of two groups. The first group received Metrazol plus vitamins; the control group received vitamins only. This study was done with thirty institutionalized women whose average age was 76.6 years. Remarkable improvement was reported in the group treated with Metrazol. These patients became more alert; their thinking became clearer; they were better oriented and improved in regard to personal relationships. According to these authors, Metrazol appears to cause the following pharmacologic actions: (1) stimulation of the cerebrospinal axis; Metrazol increases the transmission of nerve impulses and thus may behave as a general tonic-stimulant; (2) stimulation of cardiovaso-respiratory and vagal center; (3) indirect action through acceleration of circulation and improved pulmonary ventilation with an incidental increase in cerebral blood flow and oxygen supply; and (4) a possible physiologic effect of reduction in circulating lactic acid.

Wolff[140] has treated twenty-four patients with Metrazol in combination with nicotinic acid for a period of six months. The initial dosage was 200 mg twice daily. After one month the dose was doubled. The average age of these patients was 69 years. Thirty per cent of these patients improved considerably after a period of four months. They became more sociable, more alert, were better oriented, showed improvement of memory for recent events and became more interested in activities. One patient became nauseated; another one got convulsions which ceased when Metrazol was discontinued. The majority of these patients were diagnosed chronic brain syndrome associated with cerebral arteriosclerosis, with psychotic reaction.

Tennent,[141] in a recent publication on oral Metrazol, reported his experience with Metrazol in two hundred psychotic patients suffering from cerebral arteriosclerosis. According to this author, significant improvement in alertness, attitude and behavior could be observed.

Use of Glutamic Acid

Glutamic acid (monosodium l'glutamate) has been given an extensive trial for geriatric patients by H. E. Himwich, Wolff, Hunsicker and W. A. Himwich.[142] Twenty-seven patients took part in the experiment. Seventeen were judged to be improved, sixteen in regard to "action." These patients took more active part in occupational therapy and showed more interest in their work; twelve patients became more optimistic and cheerful; nine of these twenty-seven patients showed improved intellectual functioning, increased power of calculation and better memory for recent events. Eight achieved happier interpersonal relationships. They became friendlier, more sociable, more communicative and revealed better ward adjustment. Five of these patients showed a change in their thought processes, which became faster; and, finally, two revealed increased "insight" as their delusional systems became less compelling and were regarded more critically. The average age of the patients was 65. The average dosage was 10 gm, three times daily. This dosage was given for a period of three months; then for a period of four weeks placebo was used; and, finally, monosodium l'glutamate was started again for three more months. While fourteen patients were treated in this way, a control group was given placebo only and was then put on the same schedule after the first group had finished the experiment. Frequent clinical observations and psychological testing before, during and after the medication were made. Biological studies measuring the control of glutamic acid in the blood did not reveal stable increase of that substance in the blood; neither could it be proved that glutamic acid was able to penetrate the blood-brain barrier and enter the brain. However, an adrenergic action of glutamic acid and rise of glycogen in the blood appeared to be cause for the action of glutamic acid on the emotional status. Side effects were not observed in this study. One patient died suddenly of coronary thrombosis during the experiment.

Katz and Kowaliczko[143] published similar results in a study conducted with twenty-seven patients in an institution for the aged. The average age of these patients was 72 years. Glutamic acid (in the form of l'glutavite) was administered without interruption for twelve weeks, in the dose of 3.48 gm, three times a day. No untoward side effects were observed in any of these patients. Of these twenty-seven patients treated with glutamic acid, twelve (or 44%) demonstrated good or excellent improvement in regard to motor activity and sensorium. Six other patients showed a fair but noticeable improvement. Katz and Kowaliczko conclude that glutamic acid is a useful drug in the management of the elderly person in whom apathy, fatigue, mental depression, anorexia and some decline in mental function are symptoms.

Wolff[144] reported the results of a double-blind study involving thirty geriatric patients suffering predominantly from chronic brain syndrome associated with cerebral arteriosclerosis or senility. The average age of the patients was 69 years. The first group was treated with glutamic acid for three months, after which they were put on placebo for one more month. The control group was given the placebo for an initial period of three months, glutamic acid during the next three months, and, finally, placebo again for one month. Of the thirty patients in this study, twenty showed good to fair improvement, which centered around such factors as alertness, orientation, interpersonal relationships and interest in occupational and recreational activities. Confusion and verbal incoherence were decreased.

On the other hand, no significant effect on memory was observed. Side effects were mild: two patients became hyperactive; one suffered from an allergic dermatitis which improved after decrease of dosage. The dose used for this experiment was 3.5 gm monosodium l'glutamate, three times daily before meals in tomato juice.

Currier, Smith, E. H. Steininger and M. Steininger,[145] in a recent paper involving a study of glutamic acid as compared to a Ritalin® combination, reported no essential improvement in deteriorated and confused elderly patients by either medication. It appears, however, that the patients used for this experiment showed such a severe degree of deterioration, due to brain damage, that no better results could be expected.

On the other hand, Gasster[146] reported favorable response in 78 per cent of his sixty-one geriatric patients treated with monosodium l'glutamate after ten weeks of treatment. Side effects were noted in three patients suffering from cardiovascular disease. They began to show edema. This author believes treatment with glutamic acid to be superior to Metrazol. The patients treated with glutamic acid improved in regard to memory and cooperation.

Procaine Therapy

For a number of years, special research has been done at the Parhon Institute of Geriatrics, Bucharest, Roumania, in regard to treatment of the aging process. Aslan,[147] after intensive experimental studies on animals, has treated more than one hundred patients in the older age group with procaine hydrochloride, 2%, in the form of injections. The patients received injections three times daily for a total of twelve injections. Then, after a rest period of ten days, the injections were repeated. According to Aslan, the following results were achieved: regression of signs of senility of the skin, stimulation of new hair growth, improved cardiovascular reaction, better muscular power, higher production of granulocytes and globulin content, and, finally, general eutrophic action.

Kohler and Manpel[148] published improvement in arteriosclerotic and arthritic conditions by a vitamin-like action due to gradual transformation of procaine to para-amino benzoic acid and folic acid. Aslan has also noted improvement in memory, attention and various aspects of vitality in geriatric patients.

Gericke, Lobb and Pardoll[149] evaluated the use of procaine on thirty-nine patients who were 70 years of age and older. Many of these patients suffered from chronic brain syndromes with cerebral arteriosclerosis or senility and were divided into three groups of thirteen patients each. These authors used only those patients who had been hospitalized at least ninety days but not more than five years. The mental and physical condition and laboratory findings were carefully evaluated before and after treatment. These researchers came to the conclusion that procaine therapy did not cause any discernible improvement or deterioration attributable to two series of procaine injections.

Smigel and co-workers[150] chose sixty geriatric patients for an experiment with procaine hydrochloride therapy. This group included patients suffering from arthritis, nervous disorders and senile mental disturbances. Thirty patients were given procaine solution and thirty were on control solutions. Four courses of procaine therapy were administered, each one (of 12 injections) after an interval of ten days. No side effects were observed. Fifteen revealed marked improvement; nine showed moderate improvement and one showed slight improvement. These authors believed that the benefit from procaine therapy consisted in a sense of well-being, a more normal mental attitude toward self and others, greater muscular power and improved texture of the skin. They found no evidence, however, of increased libido or of reduction of the biologic age below the chronological age but believe that enough potential worth was revealed to justify continuation of the study using procaine as adjunctive treatment.

Cashman and Lawes[151] administered Gerioptil (a preparation which contains Anna Aslan's compound H3 together with a variety of vitamins and vitamin derivatives) to a group of six elderly women, using six others as controls. Their patients suffered from impaired memory and simple learning facilities, impairment of the ability to perceive and to reproduce simple visual patterns accurately and impairment of intellectual capacities. These British authors came to the conclusion that this trial failed to prove that Gerioptil was of any value to the patients.

At the V.A. Hospital, Coatesville, Pennsylvania, Wolff and Klugler[152] studied fourteen male geriatric patients involving the use of procaine injections, 2%. Their average age was 64 and their mean length of hospitalization was fourteen years. They were given three injections weekly for four weeks and then, after an interval of ten days, the treatment was repeated. Physical and psychiatric evaluation was done before, during and after the experiment. Laboratory tests included urine examination, blood count and electrocardiogram. No side effects were observed. The results of the experiment, however, were disappointing. Three patients became more alert, one of whom also became more cheerful and another one more active and cooperative. A fourth patient felt physically stronger and less fatigued and showed a better appetite and consequently gained a few pounds. None of these fourteen patients revealed any improvement in regard to orientation or confusion.

Hormone Therapy

Many studies have been made involving hormones for geriatric patients, estrogens and androgens in combination with vitamins.[153] This form of therapy is considered of value in helping improve circulation, increasing physical and mental activity and reducing fatigue. The symptoms of disorientation, impairment of memory and confusion, however, did not improve significantly. An anabolic effect was achieved but of a more temporary kind. Side effects noted were insomnia, agitation, vaginal bleeding and occasionally tenseness and soreness of the breasts (in female patients). Generally these side effects were slight. Further studies to evaluate the influence of hormone products on the mental aspects of geriatric patients are necessary and desirable.

Psychotherapy

Treating confusion in the geriatric patient must take into account the fact that confusion is not always due to brain damage but may be caused by emotional factors. A confused state in the elderly patient, with the feelings of being lost and bewildered, without permanent impairment of orientation or memory, could be a reaction to loss of a beloved object or to changes in the environment, in employment or in social status. Elderly persons resent such changes and might also become deeply concerned and confused with retirement from an occupation which has been their goal and purpose in life, or even by a physical ailment such as increasing difficulty in hearing or decreased eyesight. In such cases, supportive psychotherapy is indicated and necessary.[154] According to my own experience, geriatric patients, when confused in consequence of an emotional loss or conflict, react favorably and quickly to group or individual psychotherapy when such therapy is directed toward the goal of improving their adjustment and toward rehabilitation.

DEPRESSION AND SUICIDE IN THE GERIATRIC PATIENT

Issues of the dynamics, prognosis and treatment of the depressed geriatric patient are far from resolved. Prediction of suicidal potential attempts is still unreliable. Most studies, unfortunately, continue to treat the depression and its suicidal aspects as an encapsulated experience.

Busse[155] has made the observation that hypochondriasis is more prevalent in the older than in the younger generation. He feels that elderly individuals frequently use somatic complaints to excuse their failures and shortcomings. In this way the older individual is able to maintain self-respect and to decrease his feelings of guilt for not being successful.

Levin[156] evaluated the problems of depression in the aged and found it useful to focus not only upon internal factors but also upon external ones, which he classified into four main categories: (1) loss; (2) attack; (3) restraint; and (4) threats of loss, attack or restraint. These factors tend to occur commonly in old age. "Attack" refers to any external force which produces discomfort, pain or injury; "restraint" refers to any external force which restricts those actions which are necessary for the satisfaction of one's basic drives (especially of sexual nature); and "threat" refers to any event which warns of possible future loss, attack or restraint.

Gardner and co-workers[157] reported that a high suicidal potential exists not only in patients with psychotic depressions but also in elder patients with a problem of alcoholism as well as in patients suffering from paranoid schizophrenia. Sociological data also indicate that the probability of suicide is much higher in older males living in the lowest socioeconomic areas of the city, often alone or in social isolation and having some physical illness and a history of a disturbed work performance.

Roth[158] found ample evidence that both social stress and psychiatric disorders are involved in the increasing incidence of suicide among old people. Such factors do not, of course, operate in isolation. Social factors enhance the chances of becoming ill among those predisposed, while illness will often cause further decline in the social conditions of an old person, increasing his isolation and loneliness and forcing him, often, into an environment into which his hold on life proves to be tenuous and transient.

According to Jones and Kaplan,[159] not all suicides among older individuals can be attributed to poverty or impending poverty. The loss of a loved one often precipitates a suicidal attempt. Physical ailments are more prevalent among older persons, and some of these conditions are of hopeless prognosis. Many seek escape by suicide. Another important cause of suicide in the later decades is mental disease; suicidal tendencies are particularly prominent in involutional psychosis. While suicidal attempts may occur among senile dements and psychotics with arteriosclerosis, they are not typical of these population categories.

In order to better understand the psychodynamics of depression in the elderly person, the author made a survey of the depressive phenomena by studying the longitudinal case histories of two hundred elderly male veterans with a mean age of 64, hospitalized at the Coatesville V.A. Hospital for at least two years. All patients were depressed at the time of the study. They were categorized into two groups: those with a history of depression and suicidal episodes and those with a history of depression but without suicidal ideation. I sought to determine (1) diagnosis, (2) psychodynamics, (3) prognosis, and (4) treatment methods. This was done by a careful review of case material plus detailed interviews with patients and their families.

Results

Group A

This group contained one hundred patients with current and past history of depression but with no evidence of significant suicidal ideation or attempt. Behaviorally these patients showed psychomotor retardation in speech, gait and thinking; lack of appetite and weight gain; fatigue; feelings of exhaustion and weakness even early in the morning, with short periods of falling asleep in daytime and frequent restlessness and insomnia at night. Their general feeling tone was one of being worthless and useless, without significant goals in life, and without a meaningful program for the future; the belief that life is over and generally unsatisfactory; a lack of optimism and hope; worry and concern about financial matters, frequently of an unrealistic nature; preoccupation with health and many somatic complaints; a clinging, dependent attitude toward relatives and children; and a fear of meeting people because of feelings of inferiority and inadequacy. The majority of those patients neglected their clothing and were not clean. When the depression deepened, they typically failed to shave or comb their hair and then neglected their eating and toilet habits.

In Group A, the symptoms of depression were related to "loss" or "failure." The loss objects were as follows:

1. *Physical Health.* The majority of these patients (65%)

suffered from heart conditions or disturbances of their circulation. Indeed, after an attack of dyspnea or cerebrovascular accident with paralysis of speech or extremities, the symptoms of depression became especially intense. These patients were aware of the seriousness of their sickness, and in most of them the fear of dying was present on a conscious level. The feelings of depression, at times, were deepened by an overprotective attitude of relatives and nursing personnel and were conducive to crying spells, insomnia, increased restlessness and, in passive dependent personalities, to a desperately clinging attitude which made these patients a management problem. The other 35 per cent suffered from chronic arthritis, glaucoma, cataracts, bone fractures, severe diabetes and other crippling diseases. These sicknesses gave inadequate personalities the feelings of an even greater inferiority complex. In the paranoid personalities, paranoid ideas of abandonment by God, their own relatives and the whole world were added to the depression.

2. *Loss of Social Status and Prestige.* This included 75 per cent of all Group A subjects and centered around problems of retirement, feelings of rejection by relatives and friends, and financial insecurities.

3. *Loss of Marriage Partner and Relatives and Friends of Their Age Group.* Depressions of long duration were observed especially in patients of this group who lost their marriage partner of many years quite suddenly and who had no children and very few friends.

4. *Loss of Independence.* Forced dependency on other people, organizations and agencies was keenly felt as a severe blow to the self-esteem of the Group A patients.

Thus, the major characteristics of patients in Group A were the loss of physical health, prestige and of financial security; feelings of loneliness and isolation; a lack of life goals and increased dependency. I categorize all these dynamics under the concept of "loss" or "failure."

The basic personality structure of these patients was of a

passive-dependent nature (85%), characterized by emotional immaturity and a craving for fulfillment of their "oral needs" (of acceptance and sympathy).

Group B

This group contained one hundred patients with current and past history of depression and with evidence of significant suicidal ideation or attempt sometime in their lives. Behaviorally, these patients showed intense depression with occasional agitation and restlessness. These behaviors occurred more frequently and more intensively than in Group A. They also showed more frequent and greater irritability and hostility which extended back to early life. History of compulsive behavior and personality structure appeared in practically every subject. Of special importance was the difference in psychodynamics between subjects of Group A and Group B.

In Group B, the symptoms of depression were related psychodynamically to compulsivity. The patients' present life patterns were hard work, ambitiousness and perfection. They were interested in major details of their world and were generally rigid and inflexible. They typically showed great difficulty in adjusting to new circumstances and a new environment. They became quite disturbed and agitated about their impaired health, their decrease of prestige and social status, their diminished capacity to work and showed a panic reaction toward all features of the aging process.

Fear of dying, death and changes in their personal image were strongly emphasized in their ideation. All of them revealed features of a deep depression with the underlying feeling of resentment, anger and hostility toward other persons and toward themselves. Psychodynamically, the patients in this group had a strong Superego due to a strict education and upbringing in early childhood. They were able to repress, sublimate and/or deny their hostile feelings and their "anal character" through compulsive work. Aging with its memory impairment, decreased capacity of concentration and signs of fatigue (in association with cerebral arteriosclerosis) was particularly aggravating. Their control over their aggressive impulses became weakened. They were unable to control their hostility but yet could not "act out" against the person or persons involved. Therefore, they "introjected" their hostile feelings and became deeply depressed and even suicidal. These patients felt guilty about their hostile drives and considered suicide when the hostility and guilt mounted. Eighty per cent of the patients in Group B were found to have suicidal tendencies. In fact, suicide was later committed by 8 per cent of them. The majority of these patients were diagnosed as experiencing a psychotic depressive reaction at the time of the study, in contrast to those of Group A who were classified as psychoneurotic or psychosomatic.

Treatment Recommendation

The treatment programs for these two types of patients must take into account the described basic differences. Their needs are significantly different. Patients of Group A with psychoneurotic depression will respond to supportive individual or group psychotherapy programs. Their feelings of "loss" and "failure" must be decreased and replaced by new goals and purposes in life. They must obtain personal satisfaction and security. Stress situations (problems of physical health, finance, or social status) must be reduced or eliminated.

The psychotic depressive patient in Group B, on the other hand, should receive electric shock treatment, especially when suicidal. In these patients the goal of the psychiatric treatment should be to decrease feelings of hostility, reestablishment of control, and "sublimation" of hostility into constructive outlets. Milieu therapy (sports activities, occupational and work therapy) is indicated. Individual and group psychotherapy can also be of value by permitting these patients to verbalize their hostility. In both groups, antidepressive drugs including nialamide (Niamid),® imipramine (Tofranil)® or amitriptyline (Elavil)® are helpful. The prognosis for improvement of depressions in geriatric patients is fairly good when the treatment is meaningfully based upon their psychodynamics.

ANGINA PECTORIS AND EMOTIONAL DISTURBANCES

The American Heart Association,[160] in a special pamphlet, has recently listed the principal "risk factors" producing coronary heart disease. They involve hypercholesterolemia, overweight, hypertension, lack of exercise, diabetes and cigarette smoking. These findings have been confirmed in a clinical study of one hundred women with well-documented coronary disease at the Department of Medicine, University College, Dublin, Ireland.[161] The mean weight for this group was 13.2 pounds above their ideal weight, while hypertension and smoking were found in 80 per cent of the group.

While it is recognized that frequent attacks of angina pectoris may produce myocardial damage (with or without coronary arteriosclerosis), there is little agreement concerning the causative role of emotional factors in the development of angina pectoris. Indeed, angina pectoris as a disease entity is not essentially treated separately from "coronary attacks" in general.

In reviewing the literature on coronary disease, one finds a variety of studies and speculations. However, surprisingly little is known concerning the emotional causes of angina pectoris. Since angina pectoris is one of the cardiovascular diseases, it may be useful to review the literature on the basis of cardiovascular disease in general.

One of the first studies was done by Wolfe,[162] who described, in 1934, three cases of cardiovascular disease. This author noted the frequent occurrence of intense repressed hatred and strong guilt feelings in patients with hypertension and angina pectoris. Dunbar,[163] in 1947, referred to the "coronary personality" as consisting of compulsive striving, hard work, self-discipline and great need to get to the top. Arlow[164] emphasized the psychosomatic importance of the patient's childhood conflicts with authority in patients suffering from angina pectoris. He described an early competitive relationship with a much feared and envied parent (mostly the father). Arlow stated that the characteristic defense mechanisms used in dealing with this focal conflict were repression and identification, but they served their purpose inadequately because the patient unconsciously recreated, in new forms, the original situation of competition. He drove himself compulsively, through hard work and self-discipline, but success brought no sense of gratification or relief from tension. Arlow observed also an "anniversary reaction" in which the attack of coronary occlusion sometimes was found to occur on the anniversary of a significant event in the life of the patient. This was usually the death of some key figure with whom the patient had established a complex identification in which hostility is usually noted. According to Arlow, sexual problems, too, played an important role, including the subject's concern with diminishing sexual potency with age. Loss of libido, premature ejaculation, a feeling of growing old and compensatory efforts to prove oneself still a vigorous man are some of the problems that afflict men at this age. Russek and others[165] reported that psychic stress of occupational origin appeared to be far more significant in the etiologic picture of "coronary disease" than did heredity, prodigiously high fat diet, obesity, body build, tobacco consumption, or lack of exercise. Friedman and Roseman[166] similarly showed an increase of coronary heart disease among persons characterized by intense ambition, competitive drive, sense of time urgency and preoccupation with deadlines. Bellak and Haselkorn[167] found that patients with overcompensatory, competitive and aggressive behavior (used as a denial against excessive underlying passivity) appeared more emotionally threatened by coronary disease. For these patients, outlets for discharge of anxiety in excessive activity were denied by the cardiac disease. The resulting psychic conflict contributed further to the somato-psychological problem. Hau and Rueppel[168] reported on psychic and social factors relevant to the occurrence of disorders of organ functions as demonstrated in sixty cases of coronary disease with primarily emotional etiology. Common features of these patients were anxiety and exaggerated concern for security, inclination to avoid conflict and emotional engagement, ostensibly defensive social adjustment, lack of ability to compromise or neurotic exorbitant ambition due to a hypersensitive Ego. In the life of such a person, according to these authors, conflicts originate particularly in crisis situations related to professional position, social status and age. Inadequately solved, these conflicts result in functional disorders of various organs not rarely involving symptoms related to coronary artery disease. In an extensive study made at the University of North Carolina School of Public Health, Ibrahim and co-workers,[169] found a low level of manifest hostility with elevated levels of anxiety and repression responsible in the onset of patients suffering from coronary heart disease. Bakker[170] made observations on a group of 260 cardiac patients and observed a close relationship of certain psychological factors such as level of education, type of job and work record to symptoms of angina pectoris. His patients suffering from angina pectoris were "more wrapped up in inner urgencies and more apprehensive" than the patients without angina.

Because of the sparseness of controlled studies concerning the personality makeup and emotional problems of angina pectoris patients, the following study was begun at the Coatesville V.A. Hospital in 1966. An attempt was made in this study to see if specific emotional problems are common to patients with clearly defined, unquestionable angina pectoris disease. Can a distinctive set of psychological traits be identified in patients with angina pectoris? This study differs from the previously mentioned studies in the following ways: it was carried out jointly by a cardiologist and by a psychiatrist; anginal and nonanginal cardiac disease were carefully differentiated; patients were subjected to stressful maneuvers so that electrocardiographic responses as well as subjective responses to these stresses could be used to authenticate the presence of a genuine anginal syndrome. Such studies were in addition to routine electrocardiogram studies.

Fourteen patients proved to be authenticated cases of angina pectoris associated with arteriosclerotic coronary artery disease were selected for this study. Of these, thirteen were men and one was a woman. The ages of these fourteen patients ranged from 36 to 61 years with an average age of 49 years. Seven patients served as controls. All of them were confirmed cases of rheumatic valvular heart disease. These nonanginal controls were reported as never having experienced chest pain. Their only physical effort symptom was postexertional dyspnea. In this nonanginal group of seven patients, only one was a woman; their ages ranged from 35 to 63 years with an average age of 42 years. Care was taken not to assign persons to the anginal group merely because they experienced chest pain related to physical effort. They were considered to be genuine cases of angina pectoris only if, in addition to the symptoms, a characteristic electrocardiographic sign of myocardial hypoxia developed following a stressful procedure. In addition, four of the original patients were stressed with an intravenous injection of an ergot alkaloid. The nature of the exercise which was performed was the type generally employed in conjuction with a Master two-step test or a Treadmill stress test.[171] In connection with these tests, the postexercise electrocardiograms were obtained one, three, and ten minutes after the termination of the exercise. The electrocardiographic response to measured exercise was determined in each of the twenty-one patients; the ST segment remained isoelectric after exercise only in the electrocardiograms of the nonanginal patients.

The psychiatric investigation of these twenty-one patients included an intensive depth interview of sixty minutes' duration in order to (1) explore especially the patient's psychodynamics, (2) to determine the patient's behavior in relationship to his parents, his siblings, his wife, his teachers, and his supervisors, and (3) to establish the patient's current perceptive environmental stresses. Special attention was given to the period of toilet training, religious customs and sexual impulses especially if these were repressed. The depth interview supplemented an extensive social service history and an evaluation of monthly progress notes made by the physician who treated the patient in the hospital. Finally, prior to the patient's interview in some of the cases, special psychological tests were given.

They included the Wechsler Adult Intelligence Scale, Rorschach, Thematic Apperception Test or a Sentence Completion Test and an MMPI.

Results

The results of this study reveal that all of the angina pectoris patients suffered to a high degree from the following typical emotional features not found in the control patients suffering from rheumatic valvular heart disease. These features consist of (1) a high degree of compulsiveness, (2) repressed hostility, (3) a strong Superego (not permitting these patients to verbalize hostility), and (4) unfulfilled oral needs. Our study involved psychotic patients in a psychiatric hospital only; many of them were in partial remission. It is understood that this study still remains incomplete and is in need of more extensive controls by examination of neurotic or "normal patients," an investigation to be considered in the future.

Addendum

Since March 1967, three patients with an average age of 48 years have been treated successfully by individual psychotherapy. Their symptom of angina pectoris did not reappear after one year of follow-up study. These patients, treated by individual psychotherapy once weekly for at least four months, have been helped toward fulfillment of their oral needs, were able to verbalize hostility and gained some insight into their emotional problems. All of them tried very hard to overcome their extremely rigid and compulsive attitudes. A typical case history of a patient suffering from agitated depression and angina pectoris, treated successfully by individual psychotherapy of six months' duration, will serve as illustration.

Case History

A 59-year-old female patient was admitted to Coatesville V.A. Hospital in November 1966 after an unsuccessful attempt to commit suicide by cutting her throat with a kitchen knife. She also developed paranoid features, believing that her sister-in-law did everything possible to destroy her. Two months prior to her admission in 1966, she experienced an episode of retrosternal pain associated with profuse perspiration due to angina pectoris. The attack lasted two hours. Due to the fact that in 1966 the patient showed features of depression, confusion and memory defects for recent events, she was diagnosed as chronic brain syndrome, associated with cerebral arteriosclerosis, with agitated depression. The patient's physical condition improved with the exception of impaired eyesight, a complication the patient suffered from since 1961. Her emotional condition, treated by individual psychotherapy, showed complete remission of her psychiatric condition. Highlights of the patient's case history involve the following factors:

The patient was born in Rhode Island and was reared by a very strict and disciplinarian father. He was a chemist who died of cancer in 1948 at the age of 66. The patient remembers that the father beat her often. Her mother died in 1948, in consequence of a CVA, and is described by the patient as an "overprotective" type. The patient's husband died in 1960 of a heart attack at the age of 50. He was a restaurant owner who requested his wife to work in the restaurant, sometimes as much as twelve hours. Since 1955 she was also teaching school in order to earn additional money. The patient described her marriage as happy; however, she told the interviewer that her husband had a bad temper. Furthermore, he became interested in other women and beat her at times. After the husband's death in 1960, the patient had frequent arguments with the two sisters of the husband who did not believe that the patient should own the restaurant. Ever since the death of her husband, she said that the two sisters-in-law had been giving her a hard time and caused her to suffer from "tension headache."

The patient described herself as a perfectionist, a compulsive worker who tried to please her husband by doing a lot of overwork. She expressed little hostility throughout her life against her father or her husband. In spite of her attitude to please her husband, she found him unfaithful. Even now, she did not dare to express hostility toward her in-laws who continued to argue with her. In the past, the patient smoked two packs of cigarettes a day. She did not drink alcohol, but she was a compulsive eater, causing her to become overweight.

This patient showed the following psychodynamics: oral unfulfilled needs; a very compulsive attitude and a severe Superego which did not permit her to express hostility. She was compulsive to such a degree that she did not permit herself to relax at all.

In psychotherapy of fifty minutes' duration, once weekly, for six months, the patient learned to express hostility against her former husband, her father, her in-laws; she became secure and accepted in the protected environment of the hospital and learned to take time for recreational activities, walking, movies, reading and even dancing. She gained some insight into her condition, realizing that there was a connection between her compulsive attitude toward life and her physical and emotional disturbances.

The patient left the hospital for a local Halfway Home where she will continue to live in a semi-protected environment primarily because of her decreased eyesight. However, she is planning to live on her own and is looking for a suitable occupation. She seems to enjoy life much more than before and her outlook has definitely changed from one of despair to one of hope.

This clinical study is quite typical of the other angina pectoris patients studied and permits a more optimistic attitude for treatment and hopefully prevention of angina pectoris disease.

INDIVIDUAL PSYCHOTHERAPY WITH GERIATRIC PATIENTS

It is well known that S. Freud[172] did not favor individual psychotherapy for patients over 45 years of age. He believed that after that age the patient's character would not be flexible enough to make the necessary personality changes demanded of him once he has gained insight into his condition. Memory disturbances also were believed to represent an obstacle to treatment because the elderly patient might not be able to recall details of his childhood which would be important for the analysis. Fenichel[173] and other outstanding psychotherapists therefore preferred not to treat geriatric patients with individual psychotherapy and became, to a certain degree, responsible for the pessimistic attitude taken by psychoanalysts that geriatric patients can hardly be helped by individual psychotherapy.

Abraham,[174] however, in 1919, became skeptical of this hopeless attitude of the psychoanalysts and believed that the age of the neurosis was more important than the age of the patient. He successfully analyzed four neurotic patients about 50 years of age.

Jelliffe[175] also published satisfactory results with psycho-

analytic treatment of elderly patients and concluded that chronological, physiological and psychological age do not go hand in
hand. Alexander,[176] modifying the psychoanalytic technique and
emphasizing two different forms of individual psychotherapy,
insight therapy and supportive therapy, recommends treatment
of elderly patients with individual psychotherapy where the
Ego-strength is sufficient to handle insight-directed interpretations. He has successfully used individual psychotherapy with
older patients.

Kaufman[177] believes that the emotional rigidity found in
so many elderly persons is more a defense mechanism than an
irreversible condition and is therefore amenable to treatment.
He has successfully treated two geriatric patients suffering from
psychotic depressions. He warns, however, not to generalize his
findings and agrees partially with Fenichel that, in cases of
physically disabled patients, the neurosis might be the best form
of adjustment and therefore psychotherapy would be unsuccessful unless some external changes of the life situation would be
possible. The importance of the possibility of changing certain
life situations was also emphasized by Alexander and French,[178]
who found problems in connection with retirement, for instance, a great handicap in helping their elderly patients with
individual psychotherapy.

Grotjahn[179] has also successfully treated emotionally disturbed geriatric patients with individual psychotherapy. He
thinks that resistance against unpleasant insight is lessened in
old age and that even "narcissistic threats" for the Ego become
acceptable. Grotjahn assumes that depression and guilt in the
older patient can be relieved with the same techniques as in
younger patients through the correction of misconceptions and
unrealistic anticipation, as, for instance, the belief that old people are beyond sin and sex. The elderly subject must go through
a reverse Oedipus situation where not the son fears the father
but the aging father the son. He must work through his unconscious relation to his son. Psychoanalytic therapy has been
shown, according to Grotjahn, to be effective by interpretation
of this situation and by helping the patient gain insight.

Meerloo,[180] by analytically oriented psychotherapy, was able to help elderly patients rediscover hidden inner resources and thus to conquer their feelings of uselessness and boredom. He describes how a 76-year-old former lawyer with great memory defects started, during therapy, to study philosophy as a new hobby. With this new-found detachment from subjective complaints, he obtained a clearer grasp of the subject of logic than previously. Meerloo emphasizes the importance of environmental factors in the aged and also recommended treatment of the marriage partner or of the children when necessary. He does not recommend analysis of the resistance of the patient, since such an analysis might stir up psychotic features. He believes that the therapist as a transference figure has to replace a real loss of love and social appreciation. Carefully chosen interpretation, according to Meerloo, has, however, the same clarifying value as in the treatment of psychoneurosis in younger persons.

Weinberg[181] modifies traditional and analytic techniques and uses a more active and less formalistic approach to individual psychotherapy with the aged. He maintains that the therapist has to enter more freely into a relationship with the patient and also to manipulate, if necessary, the environment in which the older person lives. This may range from educating the family, friends, and those who are entrusted with the care of the aged concerning their needs and the detection of symptoms, to a dogged gnawing at the conscience of society to provide the necessities for a better emotional climate for our aging population.

Wayne[182] reaffirms this more active approach in geriatric psychotherapy and favors not only directing the course of therapy but also providing reassuring discussion, guidance and even environmental manipulation where indicated. He also feels that certain educational techniques, such as realistic discussions of the cultural attitude toward the aged, can be useful.

Goldfarb[183] has used a very different technique of individual psychotherapy with geriatric patients and has reported good results. His patients were treated with brief and widely spaced sessions. The maximum length of sessions was fifteen

minutes. The aim in each session was to provide emotional gratification of the patient and to increase his self-esteem. The therapist took the role of the protective parent who was strong and
powerful and able to help the patient. Goldfarb recommends
seeing geriatric patients twice within the first week and afterwards as infrequently as possible. The patients are being "fed"
emotionally and obtain strength from the therapist. After each
session they tend to feel stronger. In this way the patients win
over the potentially threatening authority figure as an ally. When
he verbalizes his resentment against the therapist but is able
to win the therapist's protection all the same by "defeating him,"
the geriatric patient feels more powerful and gains in strength.
Goldfarb considers it is important to explain the patient's difficulties to his medical, administrative and social service staff
by means of staff conferences and uses the staff's assistance to
reinforce the results of his individual psychotherapy. According
to Goldfarb, this method was not effective in psychotic patients
but was of value for psychoneurotic disorders of the aged and
for patients suffering from acute and even chronic brain syndromes. In this way, many of his patients could be treated in a
home for the aged and infirm and did not need to be transferred to a psychiatric institution.

Butler,[184] on the other hand, found the results of insight-
oriented psychotherapy involving four or five sessions a week
disappointing in the case of elderly psychotics, while Post[185] advises different methods than individual psychotherapy for geriatric patients, emphasizing three sets of causal factors: (1) lifelong personality developments within a network of relationships
with others; (2) senescent changes, especially those affecting
the brain; and (3) disorders of mood, thinking, experiencing
and behaving, probably arising from constitutional predisposi-
tions.

Since 1954 I have been able to treat a number of geriatric
patients of both sexes in psychiatric institutions, using "Brief
Therapy" as recommended by Goldfarb on psychiatric wards,
and have found it effective and useful with elderly patients
suffering from acute and chronic brain syndromes associated

with cerebral arteriosclerosis, with senility, chronic alcoholism, central nervous system syphilis (after the end of their specific antiluetic treatment) and with geriatric patients suffering from neurological disorders of various kinds. This technique definitely helped these patients to gain Ego-strength by increasing their self-esteem, by verbalizing their resentment and anger. Most notably helped were patients who were management problems on the ward by being upset, excited, threatening to other patients and to personnel; patients with poor toilet and eating habits; and others suffering from depressive features and refusing to eat. This form of treatment also brought a few delusional patients nearer reality. It was also of use in encouraging listless and apathetic patients to participate with greater interest in recreational and occupational activities and to further their socialization and rehabilitation program.

This form of therapy tended to decrease the dosage of tranquilizing medication given to patients to improve their adjustment on the ward. Occasionally, delusional patients could be induced to finally participate in group psychotherapy sessions. It was found difficult, however, to make an exact controlled study of the value of this form of individual psychotherapy on a psychiatric ward. Members of my staff reported relapses of emotional disturbances of my patients after visits of relatives, after receiving mail or after physical sickness, so frequent in the elderly population. For this reason, it was found difficult frequently to state exactly to what degree "Brief Psychotherapy" was the real cause of the improvement or what other factors were involved.

Individual psychoanalytic-oriented psychotherapy was given by myself to fifty-four patients in a psychiatric hospital with relatively favorable results.

This study is based on experience with fifty-four geriatric patients 60 years of age or over; this work was begun in 1956 and has been conducted in several psychiatric institutions. Eight of the patients suffered from schizophrenic reaction, chronic undifferentiated type and were considered "burned out schizophrenics." The other forty-six were diagnosed psychoneurotics

(30 with chronic severe anxiety reaction and 16 with depressive reaction). All fifty-four patients displayed slight to moderate symptoms of the chronic brain syndrome with partial disorientation, slightly impaired memory for recent events, and occasional confusion. All were in fairly good contact and able to communicate. They were not extremely agitated or disturbed and did not express paranoid ideas which would interfere with the individual psychotherapy.

Technical Procedure

All patients receiving individual psychotherapy were tested by psychological testing (Wechsler-Bellevue, Rorschach, TAT) prior to and following treatment. They received no psychopharmacological drugs during the study. Other drugs were given only for occasional mild physical symptoms such as common cold or gastritis. Individual psychotherapy was given once weekly for fifty minutes for a minimum of three months. However, the maximum duration was nine months. The mean age was 64 years. Eight patients were females and forty-six were males. They had all been hospitalized in a psychiatric institution three to twenty years, with an average duration of nine years. They were considered chronic and "hopeless" cases. One control group of fifty-four geriatric patients with similar symptoms received intensive milieu therapy (PM&R activities) only; another control group of fifty-four patients was treated by psychopharmacological drugs with only routine milieu therapy.

The Goal of the Individual Psychotherapy

The goal of the individual psychotherapy with these geriatric patients was to help them gain insight in order to strengthen the Ego and free them from symptoms of anxiety or depression; their "libido," previously used for repressive purposes, would then be directed toward more constructive goals. Some psychiatrists have questioned whether any insight can be achieved by patients over 60 years of age.[186]

Other psychiatrists believe that insight might be a disturbing factor and that the goal of individual psychotherapy with elderly patients should be directed more toward resocialization and environmental adjustment.[187]

In this study, the majority of the fifty-four patients were able to gain some insight into their condition. They discussed freely their feelings of depression due to physical sickness and disabilities of aging. Particularly, patients suffering from a heart condition (myocardial infarct) or with paralysis of their extremities with or without a speech defect, expressed feelings of depression. They were also depressed by increasing dependency due to physical sickness, to economic circumstances and to a decrease of their potency. In addition, impairment of memory with occasional confusion, a slowing down of concentration and attention span, signs of mental fatigue due to decreased organization of thinking, made them anxious and agitated. Great anxiety was provoked also by fear of competing with younger adults when they leave the hospital. Partial insight into these problems was achieved by forty-four patients in this study. Four patients suffering from psychoneurosis with anxiety reaction gained a high degree of insight, while the eight chronic schizophrenic patients did not gain insight at all. However, in the forty-four patients gaining partial insight, a remarkable resistance could be observed when the deepest cause for their restlessness, anxiety and insomnia was discussed. It was found that these patients' anxiety was caused by profound fear of death: they were afraid of the dark and kept the lights on all night. An attempt to make these forty-four patients aware of this psychodynamic background of their anxiety produced only greater restlessness and agitation. Therefore, the goal of helping them toward full insight had to be abandoned and replaced by an Ego-supportive technique.

The Ego-supportive psychotherapeutic method involved discussions about religion. It became evident that religion helped the geriatric patients to overcome some of their fears of dying. The patient's belief in God and in a better life after death, in heaven, was emphasized and furthered.

Special emphasis was given to improving the patients' self-esteem. Their self-esteem was found to be rather low. They thought they were "inferior" due to many physical factors caused by the aging process: impaired eyesight or hearing, chronic arthritis, circulatory disturbances, etc. They thought they were unable to compete with the younger generation due to decrease of memory and attention span or feelings of fatigue. Female patients complained about getting "old and ugly" and unwanted. The Ego-supportive psychotherapeutic technique of the individual psychotherapy had a great value pointing out the patient's assets, his emotional maturity, the importance of experience in life and in work, greater objectivity in handling persons and problems, etc. At times even a suggestive technique appeared to be suitable and preferable in handling these problems.

Furthermore, the patients were encouraged to verbalize their hostility during the psychotherapy sessions. After initial resistance, the patients talked freely about their resentment toward their children, who, at times, they believed considered them a burden. They complained about neglect, lack of understanding, about feeling isolated and about their personal and economic dependency on other persons. They felt ambivalent about not having responsibilities. They resented being treated as "babies," being pitied, being given no consideration in family affairs, and, finally, being left without purposeful goals in life. Retirement from useful work and its consequences was frequently discussed during the therapy sessions. Hostility was expressed against authority figures such as physicians, directors of welfare agencies and even against the government which, they thought, hurt their pride and lacked empathy. Geriatric patients resented being considered "second-rate cititzens" unable to find a useful occupation because of their age.

Importance of interpersonal relationships also represented an important goal of this study. For this purpose the achievement of positive transference of the patients and the avoidance of countertransference phenomena was necessary. Countertransference phenomena might become of great concern to the therapist who "does not like" a geriatric patient reminding him of his own father or mother or a meaningful figure of his past life, producing hostility in the therapist. Or the therapist, when of the male sex, might become too involved with a female geriatric patient, revealing by this attitude too great attachment to a mother-figure, therefore an unresolved "Oedipus complex" which excludes objectivity. Too much or too little involvement of the therapist therefore appeared to be an obstacle to the therapeutic procedure.

The problem of identification also plays a great role in individual psychotherapy with geriatric patients. The therapist must be able and willing to identify at least partially with the geriatric patient. Personally, I preferred the role of the understanding and supportive brother-figure in handling these patients. The therapist should convey, above all, empathy and hope to his patients and convince them that he is able to help them. At no time, however, should the therapist succumb to depressed feelings, so frequently found in geriatric patients; nor should he identify with the geriatric patient's problems of physical health. He should remind them always of the possibility of remaining effective, creative and emotionally stable in spite of age.

The study of the value of individual psychotherapy for geriatric patients always has to consider carefully the patient's assets and liabilities. The latter consist of the factors already mentioned—possible decreased physical health and strength, the feeling of being lonesome and considered a burden, increased dependency needs on other people and on the community, impaired memory, fatigue and lack of concentration (to name only the more important features). The degree of the liabilities depends very much on the individual's personality. A dependent and passive personality might become more dependent with old age; a compulsive personality might become hostile, resentful and eventually suicidal in a stress situation with old age.

Resistances and Hindrances

There can be great resistance to accepting individual psychotherapy and an eventual improvement resulting in discharge from the hospital. All geriatric patients involved in this study showed ambivalent feelings about leaving the hospital to be readjusted and rehabilitated in the circle of their own family or community. They were more or less frightened, especially after many years of hospitalization, even to be considered for an occupation outside the hospital. This kind of resistance became most evident in chronic schizophrenics of the older age group. Changes in location and environment represent a severe threat to these patients. Some of them become disturbed or show symptoms of a physical disease as soon as a release from hospitalization is considered. It is well known that schizophrenic patients of every age lack motivation to get well and suffer from bluntness of emotions and general apathy which might represent a very great hindrance for improvement.

Results

Of the fifty-four geriatric patients treated by individual psychotherapy, twenty showed no improvement and thirty-four reacted favorably. Of these thirty-four, ten could be considered slightly improved, twenty-one moderately improved and three as recovered. Generally, after twelve sessions the improvement became visible by decrease in anxiety and depression and a better ward adjustment. In four, the memory for recent events improved moderately. Of the eight chronic schizophrenic patients (6 males, 2 females), six showed greater interest in ward activities. The patients suffering from psychoneurosis, depressive reaction, improved relatively faster than the patients with chronic anxiety reaction. They showed a moderate improvement after an average of twelve sessions. Of the fifty-four geriatric patients treated by this method, twenty-two were released from hospitalization after an average of four months of individual psychotherapy, ten to their own families, eight to a foster home and four to a nursing home. One year after the end of the therapy these patients were still living outside the hospital and were making a good adjustment in their environment. They were in no need of medication or individual psychotherapy. The other thirty-two still remained hospitalized; outside placement has been considered for ten of these patients. The results obtained during the same period of time in the first control group of 54 patients treated by psychopharmacological drugs and in the second group of fifty-four patients treated by milieu therapy were of a slight degree and of temporary nature only. These patients (with the exception of two psychoneurotics with chronic severe depressive reaction) relapsed into their previous condition after discontinuation of the treatment.

Although this study is incomplete, fragmentary and leaves many problems unanswered, it does permit the following conclusion: individual psychotherapy with geriatric patients can be of considerable value. The potential usefulness of this treatment is in need of continuing investigation.

Comparison

Individual psychotherapy, in contrast to group psychotherapy for geriatric patients, presented special problems. First of all, the introduction to treatment was stormy. Twenty-five per cent revealed a great amount of anxiety and showed a relative increase of hostility in their relationship to the therapist. It took, in some of these patients, about two months to work through their hostility and mistrust for authority figures. When treatment was accepted and a more positive "transference" achieved, 60 per cent of these patients then became disturbed and agitated when "insight" was sought. The material always hovered about the problem of dying. The intense resistance and impaired Ego functioning in these patients convinced me that in all of these geriatric patients the fear of dying and their concern with the problem of life and death were best left repressed. Two of my patients discontinued the individual therapy sessions to get consolation and support from their clergymen. For this reason, I modified the goal of individual therapy. These patients were helped more by a supportive attitude which increased their self-esteem (which in many of my patients was very low) and permitted verbalization of their resentment and hostility, directed against their siblings or wives or husbands or children. Their concern with the problem of dying required a special attitude of calmness and serenity by the therapist, avoidance of overidentification with their specific fears, and a philosophy of life in the therapist which conveyed hope. The importance of their fear of dying has not yet been described sufficiently, and I wish to propose this area of universal import as a suitable challenge for treatment.

For these reasons, group psychotherapy appears to me to be more economical of time and provides treatment for a greater number of geriatric patients. Group psychotherapy is also more useful than individual psychotherapy for the geriatric patient by its specific corrective experience in improvement of interpersonal relationships, resocialization in the hospital and motivation to adjust themselves outside the hospital. The degree of initial resistance of the geriatric patient to group psychotherapy is less than to individual psychotherapy. The value of gaining insight into the psychodynamics of the geriatric patient is problematic. This is in contrast to the treatment of psychoneurotics and is clearly not always indicated for the geriatric patient.

Case History No. 1

This is the case history of a 62-year-old widowed, female patient suffering from psychoneurosis, anxiety reaction, severe, for which she was hospitalized on voluntary basis in a state mental hospital. The diagnosis was made by psychiatric examination and psychological testing. It was decided to treat the patient by individual psychotherapy only. Tranquilizing drugs or any other medication was not given. The individual psychotherapy was done by myself for the duration of fifty minutes, once a week. After each session, a report was made. The patient improved considerably after fourteen sessions of individual psychotherapy. She was much quieter, able to sleep well, felt hopeful, more secure of herself and left the hospital to take care of the household for one of her brothers and her brother's grandson. She was told to return to the hospital if and when her symptoms bothered her again. She was urged to write monthly reports about her adjustments and her feelings. After four months, a letter was received in which she let me know that she felt fine, that she had no difficulties in adjusting to her new situation, that she slept well and was praised by her brother for taking such good care of the household. Afterwards, nothing was heard from her. About one year later, news was received at the hospital by one of her neighbors who was hospitalized that the patient continued to do well.

Individual Psychotherapy Session 1

In the patient's first session she was eager to talk, was very restless and revealed remarkable trembling of her hands. She complained of being nervous and of being unable to sleep at night. She could join in activities but was upset easily and talked about another patient having a crying spell the day before, which upset and frightened her. Furthermore, she complained about being unable to concentrate. She was worried about her hair not being combed, about the heat, and said, "I have a pounding in the insides." She kept her experiences "bottled up." She talked about the treatment she had at another hospital where she had eleven electric shock treatments. She was frightened of this. She was "dismissed unimproved." "They could not do anything for me." She said that she was especially afraid of electric shock treatment because she noticed that blood vessels on the thigh of another patient had burst during treatment. She remarked that she felt more confused and nervous in the morning. In the middle of the session, she started to talk about her father who had died six years previously. When her father died, she stayed with her brother and also took care of two little boys, aged 4 and 8, who were children of neighbors. When the family of the boys moved out of town, she got arthritis. She consulted a psychiatrist who advised her to develop a hobby or other interest. However, she felt unable to do so. She talked about another patient on the ward who helped her to make her bed and upon whom she was very dependent. She expressed ambivalence about her being at a state hospital. She had dreaded coming there. "My folks," she said, "wanted me to go to a nursing home." She complained about her lack of sleep and asked the therapist if she was "hopeless." At the end of the interview she agreed to come weekly to the therapist's office "because I like to help me and to help you." She felt she got worse all the time. She could not take a bath by herself and had to be helped by the nurse.

Comment. This patient suffered from a lifelong anxiety re-action which became worse after the death of her father. Be-sides her anxiety and extreme restlessness, it was felt that her hostility was hidden but great. She was a very dependent, passive person who needed the help of others and the support of the hospital for her own feelings of inadequacy. After the death of her father, she seemed to have lost all goal in life.

Individual Psychotherapy Session 2

The patient showed less anxiety and less restlessness during the second session. She continued to talk freely about her prob-lems but tried to be evasive when her relationship to her father and mother was mentioned.

She started to talk about the movie on the ward which dis-turbed her because she did not like to see men fighting. She did not dare to leave because "I am afraid to get the worst of it." She talked about her two brothers and said that she took care of their children; but it did not seem that her "brothers had an important part in her life." She mentioned that she took care of her father after the death of her mother. Her father lived to be 91 years old. She repeated that "he had a wonderful disposition and I am a little bit like him." Her mother died fif-teen years before, because of heart trouble, and even before her mother's death she took care of her father, who could not dress himself and was weak. She bathed him frequently because he liked to be bathed by her, and he often refused to be washed by his wife, with whom he quarreled frequently. "My father looked nice when he was clean. He looked better than most other men." After the death of her father, she had a nervous break-down because she did not know what to live for. She said that she had many misunderstandings with her mother, but she did not give further information.

She also talked about her marriage and her divorce. Her husband was a salesman in a factory where she had worked as a secretary. She knew him for four years before marriage but denied having a sexual relationship before marriage. She felt bad about the divorce because she was a Lutheran and did not believe in divorce. She never tried to marry again.

She had economic worries during her marriage because her husband lost everything on the stock market during the depression in 1929. He then went to live with his mother, but she did not find this agreeable. She never had children. She did not want to have children and neither did her husband. "I never felt able to take the responsibilities." Her husband used preventive methods to keep from having children.

She remarked that she developed arthritis during the last two years when she took care of her father. After his death, she went to a medical center to get treatment for her arthritis but had to discontinue the treatment because the medicine was "too expensive."

At the end of the interview she said that she worried too much, that she could not smile, and that she was ashamed of being in a mental institution. "I feel I cannot face people when I am in a place like this. I can't relax."

Comment. It became more evident that this patient was a passive, immature person who never was able to take responsibilities and did not dare to have children. The symptoms of her arthritis started when she took care of her father. In spite of her assurances that she loved him very deeply, it was felt that she started to feel overworked and overburdened at that time but did not dare to express her hostile feelings against the father, to whom she had a lifelong emotional and erotic attachment.

Individual Psychotherapy Session 3

The patient came to my office trembling and very anxious. Both of her hands shook, but she immediately began to talk. She wanted some medicine to help her overcome her shaking and stated that she was much afraid of getting electric shock treatment. She said that electric shock treatment helped her at a medical center at the beginning, but then the doctors said that it would not help her further. She mentioned that she got upset on the previous day when one patient hit another patient with a drinking cup. The dayroom was so crowded that it was hard for her to sit there. If the other ladies went to bed, they went to sleep immediately, but she could not. She was afraid of not getting well and of staying at the hospital for a long time. She was afraid because that day was "Friday the thirteenth." Some people were superstitious because it brought bad luck to them.

Then she talked about her husband. He had died last summer, but it did not even "bother her a little bit." Her marriage was something unpleasant; she would have liked to forget it. Her husband got "awfully cross" when he lost on the stock market. "He fussed at me quite a lot." Before marriage he was good to her, also to her folks, but afterwards he thought she did not love him anymore. "We had to stay with his mother; she was old and cranky." "I told him we should have a place of our own." But her mother-in-law needed attention. For one year the patient cooked all the mother-in-law's meals. The mother-in-law did not want the husband to "give me any attention and did not like him putting his arms around me." She felt sorry for her mother-in-law because she was old and childish. She never spoke a cross to word to her.

"I feel my marriage was a mistake. If I had kept on working I might not have had this nervous breakdown." Her husband was generous with his money. They were married for eleven years; she married at 32 and was divorced at 43. By then she had forgotten her shorthand. "I was afraid to apply for another position." She stayed with her father and mother. She mentioned that she had many dates before her marriage but never had she really been in love. Her husband was a nice looking and very popular man. He belonged to a club and left her alone many nights. "I waited a long time in my car for him, watching the people go by." Now she could not sit that long anymore. Her husband, she said, was always in the company of men and frequently picked her up after a movie. She believed, however, her marriage was a happy one and, as a Lutheran, she did not believe in divorce. She did confess, however, that she did not go to church enough. "I feel badly about it now. I feel that I am getting punished for it. If I would have been a good Christian, it would not have happened."

Then she talked again about being afraid of electric shock treatment. She remarked that she was also afraid of doctors although she realized that doctors tried to help. "I am afraid to spend the rest of my life at the hospital. I want to leave here, but I want to get well before that."

At the end of the interview she inquired of the therapist what she had to do during the day.

Comment. On different occasions the patient mentioned being afraid of men and women alike. She apparently did not like to take care of her mother-in-law but never could express hostility. She remarked that her marriage was unhappy, but she still could not express her resentment toward her husband, who apparently was more interested in male company. Finally, she again showed her dependent attitude by wanting the therapist to tell her what to do and what not to do during the day.

Individual Psychotherapy Session 4

The patient was less upset and restless when she entered the office and showed less tremor of her hands. She started to talk about doctors. She was afraid of them because she might get hurt, but then she corrected herself and remarked, "I know quite well that doctors only try to help." Walking was more difficult for her than before, and she hoped that the massage she had gotten might help her. She asked for permission to drink a cola in the therapist's office, and while she did she appeared to be more relaxed than she had been the previous time. Then she said that she had no patience to sit through a movie. She also had a horror of being "locked up or tied in a chair." She was unable to smile, she remarked, because she had nothing to live for or to smile at. She also did not want people to know that she was in an "insane asylum." "It is a disgrace." She was wondering if the people who were hospitalized had ever been bright before. She had worked as a secretary for the assistant manager and had liked her work. She made mistakes but was never criticized for them. She was wondering how long she had to stay here. She pointed out that she had been disappointed when she had first come here. She could not stand the "elderly ladies," and she felt sorry that one of the patients had left for home.

Then she talked about her mother. She had died fifteen years ago and was very strict. Once, when she was 16, she wanted to go to a party, but her mother would not let her. When she wanted to ask Dad about it, her mother said that Dad had nothing to do with it. Both of her parents were born in the "old country," and people over there were very moralistic. She spent two years with an uncle who was a minister. He, too, had not been born in the United States and was minister to a church for twenty-five years. Her mother never talked about sex; such talk was forbidden at home. But, when she was 17, she read a book about it. She never knew a man before her marriage. Her husband had to support her, and she had to stay at home. "Times have changed now."

Her father liked people. "I have a good disposition just like my father. He passed away in 1951. I took care of him and even shaved him." She always kept house for him. He got up at 5 A.M. She prepared his pipe and his breakfast. Her husband was a wonderful man, too. He took care of all the bills. She never had to make decisions. "I feel that I am nervous because I cannot depend on anyone now." Her two brothers, she said, also helped her continuously. Now she could not even make her own bed. She had "arthritis" and could not move. She could not do any cooking. Her sickness came when her father passed away. Her brothers spoiled her. She hated to get up at 6 A.M. here. She did not know what to do all day long. "I am afraid of going to pieces. I sometimes feel that if I could scream it would be better. But I am afraid they will take me to one of the seclusion rooms." She had to walk up and down. She could not eat in the dining room. She could not stay long enough with other people.

At the end of the session she smiled at the therapist, said that he was a "nice man," and asked him how long he had been in the United States and where he came from.

Comment. The first sign of a positive transference became evident. The patient was less restless, talked freely about her problems and began to get some insight into her condition. She realized that her dependency upon others had something to do with her nervousness. She tried to identify with her father whom she bathed and shaved. Did she want him to be a woman? Her Superego was strong, and she controlled her hostility. Her "arthritis" was to be considered a defense mechanism. (There was no clinical evidence for rheumatoid arthritis.)

Individual Psychotherapy Session 5

When the patient entered the therapist's office, she was more tense and anxious than she had been the last time. She started to talk about the walk she had taken the previous day with the group. She noted that she could neither sit nor stand still, but that it was nice and shady outside. She said she was scared every time she had to see a "doctor." She was afraid of getting hurt. She hoped to get medicine. She could not sleep without medicine. It bothered her to eat in the dining room. She could have better table manners. She said that she still enjoyed a good movie but that she did not care for "Wild West" pictures.

"I feel so helpless; I feel somebody has to be with me all the time to help me. I feel in the morning I need somebody to comb my hair. I always worry so much."

Then she spoke about the time she attended school and also when she moved to a farm. After finishing school, she stayed two years at home and took care of her mother. Her teachers, she said, were very nice, and one of them was Swedish. She believed that she was unable to smile. When she heard the nurses laughing and saw them smiling, she wished that she could have their health. "If I could laugh and forget myself, I would be fine." She was "better off" than the other patients on the ward who had to be waited on hand and foot. Then she said she might not be able to leave the hospital. She worried that she might not be able to see her folks next Sunday. She remarked that another patient seemed not to be getting better. "When she cannot be helped, I cannot be helped, either." She was frightened of everything, especially of male patients. They cursed so much. Her toe hurt her so much that she could hardly walk. Her lower plate caused her to have a sore mouth. She wanted to get well, however. She liked it better in this building than when she first came to the hospital. She helped in the dining room but could not move fast enough. Then she talked about her mother. Her mother had a "severe look." She felt that she looked more like the mother now. She considered that she had been a burden to her brother and did not want to become one again. "Some people, when they get mad, they curse. I am a Christian; I cannot do it. I am all bottled up inside. I feel I could scream, but I take my suffering in silence." She did not keep things clean enough. Her mother and her brother reproved her for this. She felt agitated. She would like to get away soon, but she could not take care of herself.

At the end of the interview she repeated that she would not be able to talk to her folks next Sunday.

Comment. The patient was more nervous than she had been at the previous session. Her ambivalence became evident in regard to staying in or leaving the hospital. She had more somatic complaints than before. The visit of her relatives on the next Sunday had a remarkable influence on this session.

Individual Psychotherapy Session 6

The patient came into the office more relaxed than the last time. She complained about having a sore throat and said she felt "impatient." She had waited for her folks, but they had not come the day before although she had on her best dress and had done her hair well. She remarked that the preceding Decoration Day she had driven to the cemetery. There she had decorated her father's and her mother's graves. This time she was not able to go. She felt too nervous. She hated to lose her father. He was feeble and got up many times at night. Sometimes she herself had to get up every hour. But she liked to do this. Everybody liked her father, and he had a large funeral. "It made me happy that he had so many friends."

Then she talked about her mother. At her funeral there were not too many people present. Her mother suffered from varicose veins, but her death came as a blow. Her mother, she said, was cranky with her. She did not want her to go with boys. Instead, she had to go to Sunday School. Her younger brother did not approve of her smoking. He believed that she did not keep the house clean enough. Her mother did not approve of parties at night. When they had parties in her own home, the mother always had to see what was going on. Her mother wanted her "to be associated only with high-class people." She was a strict mother. She had her first date when she was 17. "My mother did not trust me. Sometimes my father said I could go, but my mother did not want it." Father and Mother, she said, frequently quarreled about it. Her mother was cranky with Dad, too. She always wanted him to change clothes when he went to town. However, he complied only when the patient intervened. She did not hate her mother. Nonetheless, she felt that mothers should be more lenient. Her father drank whiskey occasionally. Her mother did not approve of drinking.

She never kissed boys before she was 23 years old, and then only goodnight after a movie. People went in streetcars at this time and not by automobiles. She was afraid to kiss a boy because it might lead to something else. "I never was very affectionate." She felt that she was pretty as a girl. She described herself as having light brown hair and always being neatly dressed. But she did not want to get married. She liked her job too much. Every vacation and holiday she went home to help her mother. "I never kissed my father." Her father did not like to kiss her, either. She had several proposals before she was 32, but she did not want to marry a farmer. "I was a highbrow," she said, "and my chances were better in a big city." She really loved her husband. At 32 people called her "a mere angel child." She looked younger than her age. She liked to earn money and to be independent. This, she said, was the reason that she did not want to marry earlier.

She was afraid of becoming a cripple because of her arthritis. Rheumatic arthritis could not be cured, she said. She got injections for it in the past, but they did not help. "I put up a good front. I feel that I could go to pieces. I am hiding my feelings from you. I am afraid that I will get electric shock treatment. I got them at the medical center. I feel that I am being punished now and will never get into Heaven."

Comment. The patient was less tense and anxious. On the ward she related herself better to other female patients and was more interested in occupational therapy. In this session she expressed hostility against her strict mother. She revealed herself as an inhibited person who, even at the age of 32, suffered from an Oedipus complex. She rationalized liking her job better than getting married. She revealed a great attachment to her father. Father and daughter avoided kissing each other. Her severe Superego helped her to control herself. It is to be hoped that the true reasons for her failure in marriage will become more evident.

Individual Psychotherapy Session 7

The patient entered the office somewhat trembling and depressed and started talking about a cold. She had received aspirin and nose drops for it. She had to perspire so much. She remarked that she was "frightened to come to the interview today." "If I do not give a correct answer, something drastic has to happen." Electric shock treatment might have to be started, she felt.

Her brother had been here today, she remarked. She was happy to see her brother and cried when he left. This was the first time she had cried since her father's death. She had a feeling of being unable to leave this institution, but she tried to be optimistic about it. She read in the newspaper that the methods of treatment in Kansas were excellent. She told her brother that she was feeling better but that she still felt nervous. She took a ride with him in his car. When she returned she felt "kind of blue." The ladies in the wheel chair and the other ones, old ones, were pitiful to look at. She did not see that there was hope for her. "I would like to be free from these nerves, but I do not have the willpower to do things." She had been here for three months now, she said. She could not keep up with the exact date but many other patients could not do so, either. At night she had a pain across her chest. First she thought it was her heart. She was taught, however, that this pain was simply caused by nerves. The morning nurse was really sympathetic with her; she had known her for a long time.

Then she talked about her uncle (her mother's brother) who had given her a good education and had sent her to high school. She had to quit, however, because she had to go home to help her mother. She did not realize at that time that an education was more important than helping her mother. She was only 13. Her uncle did not take sides and left it up to her to go home or not. She took care of her father also. "You get used to hanging, too, they say."

She always had it easy and never had to go through what she was going through now. She believed that she should not be such a baby. Then she remarked that she looked like a tramp, but she would like to have her hair fixed. She was told that she was very attractive and she always had nice clothes. Once she had plenty of money, but now she had none.

Comment. The visit of her brother did not disturb her much, but by her somatic complaints she let the therapist know that she was unable to leave the hospital yet. She felt more secure in the hospital environment and started to gain some insight. She realized that she was immature and liked to get attention by her good looks. By taking better care of her personal appearance, she began to show some improvement. Remarking that she "got used to taking care of her father," she also began to express some of her repressed hostility. She might, however, have shifted the responsibility of taking care of her from her brother to the hospital. It remains to be seen if her brother's visit will not awaken deeper feelings in her at some future time.

Individual Psychotherapy Session 8

The patient entered the office trembling, but after a while she became quiet. "It pounds inside and outside," she said. She did not know why she trembled so much. The nurses turned the light on at night, and she couldn't sleep. When she was awake, it took her several hours to sleep again. She thought at night how long she would have to stay here and what kind of treatment she would get. Some patients told her that it was difficult to get out of here. Maybe medicine would help her. She was afraid all the time but did not know what the reason for this fear was. She was afraid of the doctors. Doctors punish people, unknowingly. She had punishment coming to her. She always had been nervous. She was nervous even before her marriage. Marriage was a serious step and a crucial one in her life. She did not believe in divorce. When she looked for a job, she was always nervous, even though she only went by recommendation. She did not like dictation at night. She was afraid that she could not read it the next day. Her husband was older than she, and she had always been dependent upon him. He became irritable and angry when he lost all his money.

She was also afraid of lightning, car accidents and of any changes in her address. The arthritis caused her breakdown. She hated to be crippled. Now she could not wear beautiful shoes as she always liked to do. If she had no arthritis, she could dress better. She was not able to fight her arthritis. She gave up. She was also frightened of talking to people. She was afraid of "not making good." Once she was married, she could not go back to her old position. She did not fight with people. Her brother told her that she could not fool a doctor. When her parents died, she could depend on her brother. She was worried about the interview, too. The therapist might lock her up. She never could hurt herself or others. She believed people always "walked over her." She did not mean anyone in particular. If she finally left the hospital, she would try to stay on her own feet. Here at the hospital they helped her. Her brother said she was too spoiled. She was worried about tomorrow. She felt bitter about being at the hospital. It was a punishment. She should fight more to get out. She was afraid to eat with other people. She could not write to any one of her relatives. She was afraid she might spend all the rest of her life at the hospital.

Comment. Again, there were some signs of insight, but her anxiety remained great and the emotional display was partially of hysterical nature. Her "arthritis" served two purposes for her: (1) to have a reason to be taken care of; and (2) to avoid expression of her hostility which was great. The therapeutic progress is slow.

Individual Psychotherapy Session 9

The patient showed resistance at coming to the interview. "I have told you everything and do not know what more to talk about." It frightened her to talk to many people. She was scared of the staff meeting she would have next Wednesday. Everything was confused; she was worried about what would become of her. She did not think she had a bright future. She would like to have her mother and father back. She regretted what she had done to them. She should have been more thoughtful. Her mother, for instance, did not want her to smoke cigarettes or to play cards. Her arthritis and her worries caused her nervous breakdown. She did not want to go to a nursing home, either. There she would not be able to have a doctor when she needed one. She did not think that she was improving. She could not marry, either, because she was not attractive any more. The days were so long. She dreaded the hot weather. She felt "like a prisoner condemned to die." She kept in contact with two friends of hers with whom she worked as a secretary. She wished that the therapist could cure her nerves and that she could go home. She would like to be a companion to an elderly lady, but now she could not even take care of herself. She did not look nice any more and could not walk because of her arthritis. She was afraid to come to the interview. When she was asked if she would like to continue talking to the therapist or if she would rather have the interviews discontinued, she said she would like to continue talking about her troubles.

Comment. The patient's ambivalence became more evident. She felt threatened to leave. However, she was less upset and restless than before and on the ward she began taking part, although with ambivalence, in ward activities. This ambivalence was interpreted to her, and she agreed with the interpretation.

Individual Psychotherapy Session 10

The patient entered the office agitated. She had visitors the day before. Her younger brother, his wife, her niece and nephew came to see her. She looked forward to seeing them, and when they left she cried a little. But at times she feared seeing them again. Last night she had slept well for the first time. However, the therapist did not realize what bad shape she was in, she remarked. She could scream, but she did not dare. She would like to be a companion to an old lady. It frightened her to come to the therapist's office. She was hurt once by a dentist. Patients told her that once they got in here they did not leave any more, but Mrs. _____ and Mrs. _____ left all the same. They were less nervous than she was, however. Maybe she did not have enough faith. Her brother told her she should not think continuously of her troubles. She would like to "blow her top." She was afraid of "getting wild." She could not lie down and relax as other patients did. If she would not wake up in the morning any more, she would be happy. Her brother's children interested her, especially her brother's grandchild. When she first suffered from arthritis, she gave up, quit working in the household. That was wrong. She could not cry and she could not smile. She wondered why the therapist was able to smile. The attendants told her she was fussing too much. She got more attention than most of the others, they told her. She worried again about Sunday when her relatives would come. When she was well, she had her hair nicely fixed and wore a beautiful dress. She did not like the day hall and the "old men" in there.

Comment. In this interview the patient was full of contradictions; however, she revealed interest in her brother's children and in her brother's grandchild. When her brother came to visit her, she received him in a beautiful new dress. She smiled at seeing her brother's grandchild and greeted the child with joy. She slept well, looked more relaxed, started to eat more and gained weight.

Individual Psychotherapy Session 11

The patient entered the office in an anxious state. She said, "I believe it is a long, drawn out affair." She felt impatient because she was at the hospital three months now and she could not get over her nervousness. She could not keep up with her looks and with her dress. She got many kinds of food she did not like, but she liked to drink milk. Changes would upset her. It made her sad to see her younger brother and his wife. They came to visit her. The other patients were not clean and cursed a lot in the day hall. Her arthritis did not permit her to walk. She could not wear shoes. She took people's troubles too much to heart. She made friends with another patient on arrival. She got along fine with her. Mrs. _____ cursed a lot when she did not help her in the dining room and worked too slow. She was even too slow walking on the grounds. If her brother would come today, she would not be ready to leave. Nerves are hard to cope with. The afternoon attendants were pretty tough. She was scared for the next day to come. She knew a lot of important people once. She had many good friends, but after her divorce she resented men generally. She did not trust men any more. She did not get such a good deal as she expected. Her father and mother were hurt when they knew about it. She liked a man to be neat, good looking and well educated. Maybe her ideas were too high. She could not face people after having been in a mental institution. She had to get over her nervous condition. Worry about her arthritis brought it on. At her birthday party, "elderly ladies" started to dance. It was disgusting to her. She was worried about how her hair was going to look. The afternoon nurses seemed to be cranky with her. She was worried about her table manners. She did not lose contact. She believed the therapist might be able to understand her and to help her more. She shook so much. Maybe God punished her for not being a good Christian.

Comment. The patient started to verbalize more hostility. She began to get more interested in her personal appearance, made friends more easily. Her thoughts began to concentrate on her brother, his family, her brother's grandchild, on a life outside the hospital. Her anxiety is decreasing. Signs of a positive transference are evident.

Individual Psychotherapy Session 12

The patient entered the office of the therapist more composed and less restless than on former occasions. She complained about being unable to sleep and not having an appetite. She worried about having lost a dress in the laundry, and now she preferred to wash her dresses herself. She was, however, unable to iron them by herself. Other patients asked to go home, but she felt that she wasn't ready yet. Everything started with her arthritis. Her brother had no room for her. She always felt she had to lean on somebody. She could not be of any help now. She worried about her hair and her looks. She could not be happy. She had a number of disappointments. She would have been better off if she had continued with her office work. It was a mistake to get married. She was in love with her husband. Many boys wanted to marry her, but they were farmers only and she did not like to live on a farm. Her mother trembled, and so did her younger brother. Her shaking was a family affair. Her father was very calm. The occupational therapist wanted her to do some painting. She was not good at that. She cared for reading only. She was especially interested in politics and read all the political articles in the newspaper. She had nothing to live for.

The last work she did was to take care of a little boy. His parents were dancers, and now they were working for a Murray studio. She took the little boy to church. She felt unable to work now. She could not cook any more. She could not even prepare breakfast. She used to bake bread and a good pie, but she forgot how to do everything. She was too dependent. She could not get interested in anything. Other patients were looking nicer than she was.

Comment. The patient started on an occupational therapy project, then discontinued, but was able to do some painting a few days later. She now dresses nicely. She started to get interested in cooking and baking and talked to the kitchen helpers. Her interest in taking care of her brother's grandchild becomes a realistic possibility. She sleeps well at night. The therapist encouraged her to take part in new occupational activities, praised her and complimented her on her good looks. She indeed looked ten years younger than on arrival at the hospital three and one-half months ago. She also started to become more interested in local and world politics.

Individual Psychotherapy Session 13

The patient entered the office complaining about the heat. She always had to carry something like a fan with her. She lost her appetite. She felt that she had not improved. She could not relax. It was difficult for her to come to the hall and do some sewing and painting. There was so much commotion. The "elderly ladies" at the dances were out of their senses. They seemed to be happy and not nervous. She wondered how long she had to stay. She could not understand why other people went home. Three ladies from her room left already. She remembered things better than they did. But the others did not get excited so much. She could now go to the dining room to eat without being scared. She was scared of doctors and "higher-up people" only. She was afraid to get lost in the city where her brother lived. It was a disgrace to come to "a place like this." A "real high-class person" did not lose her mind. She never had any desire to hit anyone, but she could not sit still. She was more of a problem than anybody else. There was nothing wrong with her physically. It was "just nerves." The nurses seemed to be happy, but she felt bitter. She was scared to see her brother again. She could not make a good appearance. She was proud, and she wanted to look nice. Talking with the therapist helped her. She could let the therapist know how sick she was. Her nervous breakdown came from worry. She had arthritis. She was afraid of becoming a cripple. She could not do any sewing, either. It was not that she did not want to, but she could not.

Comment. The patient continues to show improvement. She started to sew in the day hall and read newspapers daily. She got interested in painting but still needed encouragement. Her "arthritis" got better without medication. She was able to move the fingers of both hands.

Individual Psychotherapy Session 14

The patient entered the office in a natural way and offered the therapist a cola to drink, complaining about the hot weather. She said that she expected her brother to come to the hospital next Sunday to take her with him. She remarked that she did not like her brother, but she was interested in his grandchild, a boy now five years old who would be in need of a "better education" than her brother and his wife could offer him. She was not needed here, anyway, and did not like to stay in a room with other "old ladies" any more. Her friends at the hospital had already left, and she did not have any news from them. She did not like to be forgotten. Her arthritis got better anyway; perhaps the heat helped her hands. She perspired such a lot. The attendants told her off. They seemed to believe that she was able to do a lot of things but did not want to. She did not like to dance with the "old men" because they would ruin her new dress. The therapist alone understood her. She knew now that she did not like her mother too well and wanted to take care of her Dad alone but Mother did not let her. Her husband was nice, but he was never so intelligent as Father was. Maybe she could still find another husband. She did not feel too old yet. Everybody told her how young she looked. And she was a good cook once and would like to try cooking again.

Comment. On the Sunday following this therapy session, the patient's brother came and took her home for a trial visit to take care of his household and his grandchild, who lived in an apartment nearby, together with his parents. The therapist gave permission for the trial visit by phone and did not talk to the patient. The patient was discharged from trial visit after a waiting period of nine months in which she had made a good adjustment outside the hospital and was considered "remarkably improved." She had gained some insight into her condition by individual psychotherapy which had been supportive, too. It was felt, however, that the interest of the patient's family, especially the attitude of the patient's brother, who took her into his home and gave her a new goal and purpose in life, was of great importance in this patient's remission from her severe anxiety neurosis, complicated by hysterical and psychosomatic features.

Case History No. 2

This is the case history of a 59-year-old male patient who became depressed and anxious because of sudden changes in his occupation which he believed were humiliating for him. He also became panicky because of financial difficulties which threatened his security.

He was treated by eight sessions of individual psychotherapy with the goal of gaining some insight into his condition, helping him to verbalize his hostility against his boss, giving him support and encouragement on a new job he disliked, keeping his self-esteem high, assisting him in recognizing his limitations in a realistic way, and making it possible for him to live without considering himself superfluous and a burden for his family. With the cooperation of the patient's wife, who was understanding and sympathetic, the individual psychotherapy was a success. The patient was able to adjust himself well on his changed job; he confronted his economical situation with a new emotional outlook and found a way toward a new life with serenity and fulfillment.

This patient was seen once weekly for one hour. The patient was married, father of one boy who was graduated from college the year before, and of one girl who was graduated as a public health nurse, also the year before. The patient worked as a janitor and window washer at a power company since the previous September. Prior to this he held a job as a meter reader for about ten years but was discharged because of decreased eyesight. The patient felt tired, down-hearted, unable to sleep, and was very slow in his work. He explained his attitude of not being able to do his present job because he was not "mechanically minded and never did a job like that." He also felt angry about a reduction in salary. Furthermore, he had debts amounting to about a thousand dollars to be paid on his new house. His wife suffered from a heart condition and took digitalis daily. Although he felt down-hearted and suffered from crying spells occasionally, he did not think of suicide because "my religion does not permit it."

The patient was in good contact, oriented in all three spheres, his memory was fair for recent and remote events, and his intellectual capacities were of normal range. He was not interested, however, in reading newspapers any more and suffered from a certain apathy for the past couple of months. He was tense and anxious. His facial expression was one of depression, and his whole attitude was one of hopelessness. He was cleanly dressed, wore eyeglasses which showed that he suffered from a rather serious myopia. He looked older than 59 years. He explained that he had suffered a heart attack a couple of years ago. Ever since he had been unable to do hard work.

Diagnostic Impression. Psychoneurosis with features of anxiety and depression, moderately severe, precipitated by his change of occupation.

Comments. It appeared that the patient felt rather ashamed of his present status and suffered from an inferiority complex. He had felt humiliated and could not confront his son and daughter, who had a higher education than he did. Individual psychotherapy was indicated. No tranquilizing drugs were ordered.

Individual Psychotherapy Session 1

The patient returned in time for his first psychotherapy hour. He was tense and anxious and complained that he was unable to concentrate. He had felt himself "going to pieces" the day before. He cried "like a little boy" and believed that he would not be able to get up in the morning. Asked how he felt about coming to the therapy hour, he answered that he had no "pro or con feelings," but he did not resent it. Then he continued to talk about his present job and how important it was for him to keep the job. But he had no interest in it. He used to be interested in politics, but he did not read newspapers any more. Then he remarked that his wife suffered a heart attack the same morning. He felt very helpless. All he could do was to pray. He had no willpower left. He lost faith in himself and could not sleep the night before. He complained that he did not like his present job because he was not used to "mechanical instruments." He mentioned that his boss always had been good to him, and he did not understand why he had to do manual labor now. He expressed some hostility against his boss. At the end of the hour he said that he always had been a perfectionist and much concerned about himself. Now he was going through a "living hell." He also had a bad time as a child when his father and mother died. At the present he felt like wanting to die.

Individual Psychotherapy Sessions No. 2 and 3

The patient returned regularly for his appointment. On this day he was tense and frightened and said he would like to crawl into his bed and not get out any more. He had to force himself to do anything. He felt hopeless. He was avoiding seeing people. Before this demotion happened, they called him the "main street philosopher," but he did not feel like that now. He was praying every day. It was a "torture" for him to go to work.

A week later the patient seemed much more relaxed and relieved. He still showed a compliant attitude, excused himself for not closing the door, stated that he took the psychiatrist's time but asked to smoke a cigarette and talked much more at ease. His main worry was the fact that he bought a new house but had not sold his old house yet and this time had two bills to pay for light and for other things for the new home which was still empty. He reproved himself that he did not sell his old house first before buying the other one. While he smoked a cigarette he remarked that he shouldn't smoke because he

could not afford it. But he continued, "The Lord will help me."
He did not despair any more. Then he said that he felt a certain amount of guilt because he had not been an "angel." He
always tried to be a big shot, only he could not be one. At the
end of the interview he said that he always liked to read ad-
venture books and Westerns but had not done this for a long
period of time. Now he felt like going to the library again.

Individual Psychotherapy Sessions 4 and 5

The patient returned promptly for his fourth outpatient appointment and immediately started to complain about his two
houses which he "had on his neck." He was unable to sell one.
Then he said that he read a book which he had at home about
the Korean War, but he did not enjoy reading it. He tried to
"analyze himself." He would like to know how much of his
trouble was physical, owing to his age, and how much was
bad will. He believed he had signed the contract for his new
house. Then he talked about his boy who changed his job. He
was now on the personnel staff of a college. He remarked that
he went shopping but avoided meeting people. At the end of
the interview he was more cheerful and started to smile. He
made the remark that although he was worried, he did not
worry about his funeral yet.

At the next meeting, he looked more relaxed. He mentioned
that he could hardly wait to come to his therapy hour because
"the therapist was so understanding." Again he talked about his
houses and said that he couldn't figure things out. However,
he was getting along better with his work; nobody complained
about him or said anything negative. He remarked that he
smoked two packs of cigarettes a day and felt that was too much.
He could do better things with the money than spending it on
cigarettes; he could go to a movie once in a while. He read a
new book, *The Robe*. He liked it very much. Then he spoke about
his job. He did not like the physical effort in connection with it
but did not want to quit because he would be getting a pension.

He went the previous Sunday to town to see his son-in-law.
He watched a movie on television about a treasure buried dur-

ing the Civil War in New Orleans. He went away relaxed and in a good mood.

Individual Psychotherapy Sessions 6 and 7

The patient returned for outpatient psychotherapy the following week. He remarked that he had nice holidays, watching television and attending church. He still did not feel completely relaxed. Then he talked about his experiences as a "house servant" in Germany after World War I. He liked the atmosphere of his job and got a lot out of it. He never wanted to be quite dependent but liked to stay employed. Then he spoke about a heart attack he suffered a few years ago, together with pneumonia. He bought only one new suit of clothes since he married. He did not like to spend money but thought he now spent too much for cigarettes. He realized that changes upset him and that he had difficulties with "technical advances." He thought he made friends easily and would have been very good in "public relations." He did not like jazz music but preferred "good music" only.

The patient returned the following week and appeared relaxed, more secure of himself and in a better mood. He read some books and watched television. He spoke about the Americans treating minorities badly and how unjust this was. He then made remarks about consumers and production and went on talking about political matters of the day.

Comment. It appeared that he wanted to impress the therapist with his general knowledge about politics. The patient apparently had overcome his depression. He was much better adjusted on his present job. The therapist talked to the patient's wife, who was waiting, and encouraged her to have patience. She left in a hopeful mood.

Individual Psychotherapy Session 8

The patient returned the following week. He saw books on aging on my desk and remarked, "That's for me. I felt it during the last few months." He was less tense. He stated that he had four people interested in buying his old house, but his wife agreed now that they had been hasty in buying the new house. Then he told about a book he read about Buffalo Bill. He was the last of the great scouts and killed 40,000 buffaloes. He continued saying he could not complain too much and that he was "back to normal" again. His aspect was one of a man looking younger than he had looked; the features of depression were gone.

He was proud that his son was elected to the staff alumni association of a college. He said that once he met the mental health director at the same college at a private party. Both his son and the director's son were students. He said that the only difference between the director of mental health and himself was "I have no money." Then he laughed.

Comment. The patient had completely recovered from his features of depression and anxiety and was released from psychotherapy; he was told to return to the hospital and get an appointment at some future time if needed. He did not return. His wife let us know six months later that he was well adjusted on his new job and "felt fine."

A SODIUM AMYTAL INTERVIEW

This is a Sodium Amytal® interview of a 75-year-old patient who suffered from a chronic brain syndrome, associated with senility, moderate, with features of a neurotic depression. The patient improved with group psychotherapy for three months. He was transferred to an "exit ward" but fell down and received a fracture of his leg. He again became depressed, refused to eat and was uncommunicative. With his permission, a Sodium Amytal interview of about twenty minutes' duration was given to him to find out the psychological cause of his depression. It was suspected that he felt ambivalent about staying at the hospital or leaving it. He would have to take care of himself but considered living with his son.

The Sodium Amytal interview was given in the presence of the head nurse and psychiatric nurse in charge of the ward.

Doctor: What happened to you? How did you fall?

PATIENT: I was on the ward. I broke my leg and they sent me to Kansas City, and then they brought me back. They had me in a cast for a while.

DOCTOR: How did it happen that you broke your leg?

PATIENT: Well, sir, it seems awfully silly. You know they have rollers on the legs of the beds and some of the rollers have brakes on them and some of them don't. Well, sometimes they are not put on and the bed will roll. One night I got up and wanted to go to the bathroom. I reached under the bed to get my house shoes and the brakes were not set and I slipped out and broke my leg.

DOCTOR: When did you come back to this hospital?

PATIENT: I don't remember. Time flies.

DOCTOR: Why did you come back?

PATIENT: I don't know. They sent me.

DOCTOR: Did you drink?

PATIENT: Yes, sir, a little bit. That was years ago. I do not drink to excess.

DOCTOR: How long ago was that?

PATIENT: Oh, I would say about ten years ago. It seems about that long.

DOCTOR: Why did you start? Were you unhappy about something?

PATIENT: Oh, I just drank socially.

DOCTOR: Could you not stop?

PATIENT: I did.

DOCTOR: But, Mr. _____, why did you come back here to the hospital?

PATIENT: I got sick and came back. I came back because I wanted to. I was here before and I had no place else to go. I could not afford to go to a private clinic.

DOCTOR: Why did you not go home?

PATIENT: I have no home.

DOCTOR: Who took care of you before you came here?

PATIENT: I took care of myself.

DOCTOR: How did you feel about that?

PATIENT: Oh, I worried about things—money and things.

DOCTOR: You lived alone?

PATIENT: Yes, my wife died in 1935.

DOCTOR: Do you have any children?

PATIENT: Yes, I have a son and a daughter. My daughter died.

DOCTOR: Why don't you go to your son?

PATIENT: They don't want me. They have a nice home but my daughter-in-law does not want anyone to live with them. She would not let her own father live with them.

DOCTOR: Why does she not want a nice gentleman like you?

PATIENT: I don't know. She is just that way.

DOCTOR: Does your daughter-in-law not like you?

PATIENT: I don't think so.

DOCTOR: What does your son do?

PATIENT: He works for a creamery.

DOCTOR: Does he earn good money?

PATIENT: Oh, no. They have bought a new home. They bought it "on time"; he still has to pay for it.

DOCTOR: Do you have only one son?

PATIENT: That is right.

DOCTOR: When you fell in the other building, did they want to send you out of the hospital?

PATIENT: (Did not answer.)

DOCTOR: Were you excited or nervous?

PATIENT: No, I got along well.

DOCTOR: Why can't you live on the outside?

PATIENT: I don't have enough money. I only get seventy-five dollars a month.

DOCTOR: You can't live on that?

PATIENT: No, sir.

DOCTOR: How much rent do you pay?

PATIENT: I paid twenty dollars a month. I got along well, but I got sick. I wasn't myself, and so I told my son to bring me here.

DOCTOR: What should we do here to help you?

PATIENT: Get me perfectly well and walking. I'd like to go home again.

DOCTOR: What would you do at home?

PATIENT: I would cook and eat and live.

DOCTOR: Have you always been alone?

PATIENT: No, I was married.

DOCTOR: Do you miss your wife very much?

PATIENT: Very much! She was a fine woman, a very good woman. We lived together a great number of years.

DOCTOR: Were you always happy?

PATIENT: Very happy.

DOCTOR: What happened to your daughter?

PATIENT: She died of a gunshot wound. She committed suicide. My wife died of cancer, and my daughter lived with the fear she would get it.

DOCTOR: Did she get it?

PATIENT: No.

DOCTOR: Was your daughter married?

PATIENT: No.

DOCTOR: Did you ever think of killing yourself?

PATIENT: Oh, no. I want to live. Even here I am not too unhappy.

DOCTOR: What can we do to make you happier?

PATIENT: I can't think of anything. I would like to get rid of the pain in my leg.

DOCTOR: What was your occupation before you came to the hospital?

PATIENT: I used to be a cook. I was a very good chef. I worked many years.

DOCTOR: How did your health get bad?

PATIENT: Oh, it was not my heart. Cooking is unhealthy after a time. After I worked for a cement company I bought a restaurant. I couldn't get enough help. I worked too hard and I got sick.

DOCTOR: Where is the restaurant? Did you sell it?

PATIENT: Yes, I got sick and had to sell.

DOCTOR: Why did you come to this hospital? Don't you know this is a hospital for "mental" patients?

PATIENT: Yes. There is nothing wrong with my mind. It is pretty good, you will have to admit that.

DOCTOR: Is your son interested in you?

PATIENT: I think he is interested, but he does not want to keep me. They have a little girl taking piano lessons and a nice home. My daughter-in-law does not want her own father there.

DOCTOR: Do you have any friends?

PATIENT: I suppose so.

DOCTOR: Why do you not go to stay with your friends?

PATIENT: Oh, you don't go to friends. I would not ask them to do anything for me.

DOCTOR: Are you too proud?

PATIENT: I seem to be. I have always been a good man and lived clean.

DOCTOR: You say you lived a clean life. Did you drink?

PATIENT: A little bit.

DOCTOR: Have you been drunk?

PATIENT: I have been a little tight, but never drunk.

DOCTOR: Did you go to church?

PATIENT: Yes.

DOCTOR: Did you ever commit any crime?

PATIENT: No, I never committed any crime at all. I have always meant well to other people.

DOCTOR: What about your daughter-in-law? Do you like her?

PATIENT: Yes, I like her.

DOCTOR: Are you sure?

PATIENT: Absolutely.

DOCTOR: Do you think your son is a good son?

PATIENT: He is a fine son. A good boy.

DOCTOR: When did your wife die?

PATIENT: In 1935.

DOCTOR: How did you feel?

PATIENT: Very badly.

DOCTOR: Did you ever consider marrying again?

PATIENT: I thought about it, but my fiancee died.

DOCTOR: How long ago was that?

PATIENT: Three years ago.

DOCTOR: How old was she?

PATIENT: She was not young. She was 60. She ran a store and did very well. She was a very efficient woman.

DOCTOR: What did she die of?

PATIENT: She died of a heart condition.

DOCTOR: What about your future?

PATIENT: I'll wait and see how I come out. I want to get well and not be crippled up.

DOCTOR: Do you feel lonesome?

PATIENT: Yes, sometimes.

DOCTOR: If you get well, what will you do then?

PATIENT: I'll try to go home again. I am just so short on money. I got behind, but I am paying to catch up. I am paying to the state. I feel I owe it.

DOCTOR: Were you a good worker?

PATIENT: All my life.

DOCTOR: Did you ever want to die before you wife died?

PATIENT: No, I wanted to live.

DOCTOR: If you live twenty years more, what would you like to do?

PATIENT: I don't know. I am too old to do anything. I am 75 years old. Nobody wants a 75-year-old man. You will find that out when you reach that age.

DOCTOR: What do you think of a nursing home?

PATIENT: I do not think I have enough money to do anything.

DOCTOR: Do you need treatment for your mind?

PATIENT: No, sir. There is not a damned thing wrong with my mind.

DOCTOR: Other people thought so, didn't they?

PATIENT: Well, they are wrong.

Comment. The Welfare Department of the State was advised about the patient's condition and checked into his and his son's financial condition. It was decided to have him transferred to a nursing home where Public Welfare would pay full maintenance. The patient left the hospital after two months when he was able to move around. Successful surgery was performed for his leg fracture. The patient's progress in the nursing home was carefully checked. He adjusted well and was not in need of further help from the hospital. His depression subsided completely when he became interested in another "nice lady" at the nursing home.

TECHNIQUES OF GROUP PSYCHOTHERAPY WITH GERIATRIC PATIENTS

Group psychotherapy was attempted with geriatric patients by Silver[188] for the first time in 1949. He explored the treatment possibilities of seventeen female patients between the ages of 70 and 80 years at the Verdun Protestant Hospital, Montreal, Quebec. The group met twice weekly. Of this group of seventeen, five were classified as senile psychosis, paranoid; three as senile psychosis, confused; two as senile psychosis, presbyophrenic; two as senile pychosis, simple; one as senile psychosis, depressed; three as psychosis with cerebral arteriosclerosis; and one as psychosis with hypertension. The most discussed topic was the patients' desire to go home. Their unanimous preference was for living with their own people rather than living with people of their own age in a nursing home. Other thoughts occupying their minds centered around the following problems: (1) physical complaints; (2) the good old days; (3) socioeconomic factors (the patients revealed a distressing awareness of these factors which caused them to feel a great insecurity); (4) loneliness (with many of the patients, all known relatives and most of their friends were dead, and they were acutely aware of being alone and helpless); (5) wishful fantasies (these were mostly of the grandiose kind); and (6) rejection (in some cases, rejection of these patients by their families was quite obvious).

Silver found that group psychotherapy with senile psychotic patients improves ward morale, particularly for nurses who see an active treatment program attempted on the old patients. Furthermore, improved behavior, greater cleanliness, better eating habits and less confusion in these patients was reported. Relatives finally came to discuss possibilities for the patients to leave the hospital.

Schwartz and Goodman[189] used group psychotherapy with

obese elderly diabetics in 1950. A group of nineteen overweight patients, consisting of fifteen women and four men, in the Diabetes Clinic of the Outpatient Department, Mt. Sinai Hospital, Cleveland, Ohio, was organized into an obesity class. All but two of the patients were over 50 years of age, with 78 per cent over 60. Duration of diabetes in these patients varied from four months to thirty-five years, with an average of about eleven years.

A weekly one-hour session was held for the period of one year. The caloric value of foods, the role of emotions in obesity and the adverse effects of obesity were discussed. Prior to group therapy, only two patients were less than 10 per cent overweight. At the end, eleven individuals were less than 10 per cent overweight. Five of these had reached ideal weight. Average loss in weight was 15.8 pounds. In addition to weight loss, certain other favorable results were obtained. Two of the seven who were taking insulin at the beginning were able to discontinue it entirely. Three needed a smaller dose.

Intense education efforts were also of great value. However, more important than any of these were (1) the feeling of identification with the group in relation to a mutual problem and (2) the relationship of the individual to the group leader.

The authors conclude that the group therapy method yields worthwhile results in many cases resistant to the usual management of obesity employed in the clinic.

Benaim[190] carried out an experiment on the male ward of the Geriatric Unit of Bethlem Royal Hospital and published his results in 1957. The group consisted of between seven and ten members, meeting once a week for an hour and a half. The method of treatment was nondirective; the therapist assumed a passive role. During the five months in which the experiment was carried on, eighteen patients attended the group.

The average age of the members of Benaim's group was 68 years. The diagnosis of these patients varied from manic-depressive psychosis,[13] cerebral arteriosclerosis,[1] schizophrenic reaction,[1] paranoid state[1] and psychoneurosis.[2]

Benaim reports that as time passed, a strong group feeling

developed, characterized by mutual support and critical evaluation of each other's progress. Emotional upsets within the group
were not infrequent—members verbally attacked each other with
great vehemence, later apologizing and parting friends. Benaim
concludes that, though this project was brief and uncontrolled,
it led to a happier atmosphere in the ward and more sociability
and contentment among those who took part in it. Benaim
recommends. that group therapy be extended to geriatrics units,
day hospitals, outpatient departments and other places where
geriatric patients are in treatment.

A more controlled and extensive study has been made by
Linden[191] at the Norristown State Hospital (Pennsylvania) during the years 1949 to 1954. Linden gives the following criteria
for selection into group psychotherapy with geriatric patients:
(1) expressed desire to join the group; (2) appearance of relative alertness; (3) a fair degree of good personal hygiene; (4)
ability to understand English; (5) ability to walk or be wheeled
to the meeting room; (6) at least a minimal range of affects; (7)
evidence of some degree of adult adjustment prior to entrance
into senile state; and (8) capacity for evoking interest and affection from nursing and attendant personnel.

The group consisted of fifty-one senile women. The development of group solidarity was very slow in showing itself.
The first noticeable effect was a pronounced change in atmosphere throughout the building. The traditional atmosphere of
pessimism, inactivity, stagnation and futility began to be dissipated.

At the beginning the group leader was the male ward physician. After six months this was changed to dual, male and female, leadership. The female leader was a ward nurse who
had been auditing the group meetings. Mutual support and
protectiveness were outstanding dynamisms as the group progressed.

Early in the group process an effort was made and sustained
for a few months to encourage free association, uninhibited public expression and mutual interpretations. Later on it was found
that the rotation method of calling on as many members as

possible and questioning them about some biographical items was more stimulating, yielded fewer embarrassing silent periods and kept the group alert. Much later on, an educational element was introduced with members volunteering to prepare ten to twenty minute presentations on subjects of group and seasonal interest.

Linden reports the following results: Of his group of fifty-one women, twenty-three (40%) left the hospital for their own homes, county homes or foster homes, or were felt to be ready to leave after an average of fifty-four hours of group psychotherapy. Linden used a control group of 279 other geriatric female patients who did not receive group psychotherapy. Only twenty-seven (10%) of these were released from the hospital.

Rechtschaffen, Atkinson and Freeman[192] described their intensive treatment program for geriatric patients at the Fergus Falls State Hospital (Minnesota) where group and supportive individual psychotherapy were utilized along with an organized ward program which included occupational, recreational and work therapy approaches. These investigators selected 110 patients from a total of 312 by means of two prognostic criteria: the behavior level of the patient and the amount of interest in the patient shown by relatives.

The average age was 72 years, the average length of hospitalization ten years. The majority of these patients carried the diagnosis of senile psychosis (46%) and psychosis with cerebral arteriosclerosis (33%).

Group psychotherapy was carried out for one hour twice a week for the duration of one year. Psychologists, social workers and recreational therapists shared the leadership of the sessions which ranged from insight-provoking talks on problems of growing old and of being in a state hospital to general discussions of politics and hunting and fishing.

Results of the program were far beyond original expectations. The program resulted in a 38 per cent increase in the discharge rate. Forty-six patients left during the first six-month experimental period; only five of these returned for hospitalization. Of the forty-six patients who were discharged, twenty-two went to live with relatives, nine to live in private rooming houses and fifteen to live in rest homes.

Self-morale and optimism regarding treatment of the aged increased greatly and proficiency in dealing with elderly patients improved.

My own experience with group psychotherapy for geriatric patients dates back to September 1954 when group psychotherapy was started in a Kansas state hospital affiliated with the Menninger Foundation. Since then, I have continued this form of treatment with geriatric groups at the State Research Hospital in Galesburg (Illinois) for the period of one year, and, finally, for ten years at the Coatesville V.A. Hospital.[193]

My technique is different than Linden's and involves both male and female patients. Since the beginning, my groups have been composed of three or four men and three or four women, although in recent years I have also been conducting an all-male group.

Criteria of Selection

The patients were selected after careful consideration of their physical and mental condition. Geriatric patients with too many physical complaints were excluded because of the possibility of sudden death or chronic sickness. Those chosen were able to hear and to see fairly well. They were in fairly good contact with their surroundings, not overtly psychotic and did not suffer from delusions or hallucinations.

During a period of more than fifteen years, in three different psychiatric hospitals, 340 geriatric patients were treated by this form of group psychotherapy. The sessions were of fifty minutes' duration, once weekly.

Diagnoses of Patients

The diagnoses of the patients were of minor importance. They varied among chronic schizophrenic reaction (40%), chronic brain syndrome associated with cerebral arteriosclerosis (20%), with senility (18%), and chronic brain syndrome associated with alcoholism, luetic infection and others (22%). One-fourth of the schizophrenic patients had a chronic brain syndrome due to the cerebral arteriosclerosis or senility. Thus, a total of 70 per cent had organic brain disease. Of these 340 geriatric patients, 42 were females. All patients were evaluated prior to the beginning of the group psychotherapy sessions by psychiatric examination and psychological testing, which was repeated at six-month intervals.

Thought Content of the Patients

Very interesting studies could be made in regard to the thought content. The most frequent topics chosen for discussion by members of the group were (1) religion, (2) marriage and love life, (3) historical events and (4) food.

Religion was the preferred topic of the members of the group. Unhappy, lonesome and despondent patients were eager to discuss a better life after death. The religious attitude increased when the personality disintegrated and became disorganized. Religious belief and faith in God helped them to overcome their grief and gave almost all of them support and greater Ego strength.

Nearly all married patients expressed deep attachment to their spouse. They showed anger against them only during the acute phase of their sickness. Hostility toward their children was a more frequent topic for discussion. Resentment and feelings of being rejected and a burden to the younger generation were ventilated. They felt somewhat relieved to know that other members of the group had suffered troubles of a similar kind. Thus, they came closer to one another and their interpersonal relationships improved remarkably. Erotic feelings were repressed at first, but after a couple of months, the men and women looked at each other with affection. They started to dress with more care. The men shaved more regularly, came to the meetings with their best ties and washed themselves more frequently. The ladies began to use lipstick and to powder their faces. This change in the patients' attitudes toward their personal appearance was one of the first good responses to group psychotherapy.

Unless physically sick, the geriatric patients in my groups liked to eat and showed a certain amount of regression to the oral stage. Consequently, one of the most important topics of discussion during the meeting was food.

While for the elderly patients in state mental hospitals, religion, marriage, love life, historical events and food were the most frequent topics of discussion, the patients at the Coatesville V.A. Hospital were more interested in daily political events and in the current economic situation. Most of them read the newspaper daily and watched television. At times, they distorted political facts. On these occasions, they would get angry and excited and ventilate hostility. Frequently, they tried to rationalize their own feelings of insecurity by considering themselves victims of unfortunate circumstances.

Results

Of the 340 patients of the elderly age group treated by group psychotherapy, 40 per cent showed improvement and were released from hospitalization. The improvement became evident three months after the group sessions were started. Generally, six months of treatment were necessary to secure a better emotional equilibrium. About 10 per cent of the patients needed more than six months but less than one year before they were released from hospitalization. The patients started to verbalize their feelings, were able to control their hostility better and made a better ward adjustment. They started to communicate with one another more than before, made friends and took part in occupational and recreational activities together. Some of the patients who had been confused and out of contact at times now talked more coherently. Others lost their paranoid ideas which they had expressed occasionally. Doubts by other members of the group about their persecutory delusions helped them to come nearer to reality.

According to my observation, the sex of the patient did not

make any difference with regard to improvement. However, group psychotherapy sessions given to geriatric patients of both sexes was definitely of greater curative effect than that given to control groups with only male patients. The increased interest of male and female patients in each other, the verbalization of motherly feelings of the women toward the men, and the protective attitude of the male patients toward the females had a remarkably therapeutic advantage. Follow-up studies were done after six months and one year and confirmed the stability of the patients' improvements by group psychotherapy which made it possible for them to adjust outside the hospital. After their release from hospitalization, only three patients returned for additional group psychotherapy sessions once a week for the duration of four months.

Other control groups, comprising patients who were treated by occupational and recreational activities alone, without group therapy, revealed the superior value of group psychotherapy with geriatric patients as a therapeutic tool. The improvement of patients in these control groups was of a minor degree only.

Goals and Limitations of Group Psychotherapy with Geriatric Patients

According to my experience, anxiety decreases in group psychotherapy, transference to one or more members of the group is easy to achieve because of the variety of choices, and meaningful discussions are possible because a common goal or interest can be found with less effort. In a group of geriatric patients, the patient who tends to distort the therapist into a fear-inspiring figure feels the presence of others to be protection for him. Acceptance by the group is, at times, very important to a patient. Furthermore, feelings of difference and isolation decrease because the patient's problems are shared by others.

Furthermore, each member of the group is helped to grow toward a higher level of emotional maturity. Negative transference in the geriatric group becomes apparent at times between single members of the group and the therapist or between members of the group themselves. Countertransference phenomena might become of concern for the therapist who does not like a patient who reminds him of his own father or of an important figure of his past life, producing hostility in him. Such countertransference phenomena can easily become an obstacle to therapeutic progress. The problems of identification are also of great importance in geriatric group psychotherapy. If members of the group are able to identify with others in the group, this would be beneficial, influencing the whole atmosphere of the group. Identification by the therapist with his group represents a great advantage. For this purpose, the therapist for a geriatric group should not be too old or too young and should be in good emotional equilibrium himself. The therapist should convey, most of all, empathy and hope to his patients.

Another much discussed problem in regard to group psychotherapy with geriatric patients and its therapeutic aim is the gaining of insight. Some insight can be achieved through group psychotherapy. Some therapists are inclined to de-emphasize the gaining of insight but emphasize resocialization and the return to a higher degree of self-sufficiency. According to my experience, the development of deep insight for elderly citizens is frequently not only impossible but also undesirable. Geriatric patients reveal, at times, a certain inflexibility of character and attitude because of increasing age. They also often suffer from impaired memory as part of brain damage due to pathological changes in the brain substance itself and forget some important events of their lives. Other problems involving insomnia and restless agitation are expressions of their fear of dying. Letting elderly patients gain insight into this specifc condition might disturb them greatly and can increase their symptoms. Support, rather than insight, is indicated and is more helpful on such occasions.

Group psychotherapy is of definite usefulness to geriatric patients when the focus is placed on increasing the amount and the quality of socialization, group identity and self-expression. Repair of the underlying personality conflicts is possible and advisable only in limited ways.

MILIEUTHERAPY

Occupational Therapy with the Geriatric Patient

The importance of an active occupational therapy program for the chronically ill and the aged has been described by Knudson,[194] Ferderber,[195] Blustein[196] and others. The Veterans Administration has recognized the value of occupational therapy for the rehabilitation of the geriatric patient and is now striving to improve occupational therapy activities in a progressive rehabilitation service in its hospitals throughout the country. Important research has been done at the V.A. Hospital in Downey, Illinois, and the good results of the new approach in regard to the treatment of geriatric patients have been described by Blustein. Blustein recommends a special occupational therapy program for elderly veterans using many varieties of handiwork with simple tools and devices. These include leather work, woodworking, basketry, weaving, painting, knotting, hooking rugs, knitting and copper tooling. Their attention span was limited to forty-five minutes. Library clubs were started by librarians for the purpose of giving book reviews and discussing current events. The patients helped in special assignments on the wards: making beds, helping others to make beds, arranging linen in the linen room, mending clothing, dusting areas around their bed. Hobbies were encouraged such as keeping scrapbooks, making joke books, cutting out cartoons and pasting them in books. An aquarium was maintained on the ward, and interest in nature study was encouraged.

At the Sepulveda V.A. Hospital, an excellent work-oriented occupational therapy program has been described by Pearman and Neuman.[197] This project is particularly designed to reach older patients who are withdrawn. They performed contract work consisting of counting, packaging and boxing small toy items for shipment, for two and one-half hours each morning, five days a week. They also did volunteer work for community agencies such as counting and folding printing materials, stuffing envelopes and preparing them for mailing. Group outings financed by their earnings promoted socialization and a sense of identity with the group and the community. They had strong feelings about belonging to a group and pride in their ability to do productive work.

According to my own experience with occupational therapy with geriatric patients in psychiatric institutions, I have found an active occupational program of great usefulness, and I strongly recommend it.

Occupational therapy for geriatric patients in mental institutions and clinics has been prescribed for many years, but usually only for its physical or orthopedic benefits. This kind of occupational therapy was directed toward the maintenance of bodily function in patients with rheumatoid arthritis or hemiplegia, toward the rehabilitation of patients with fractures and toward improving circulation, the function of muscles and joints and coordination in neurological diseases.

Today, occupational therapy is employed more for its benefit in alleviating psychological and sociological problems. G. S. Fidler and J. W. Fidler[198] believe that occupational therapy is "a set form of psychiatric treatment which uses constructive activity as a modus operandi." W. C. Menninger[199] recommends hobbies and recreational and occupational therapy to release tension, to compensate for real or fancied inadequacies, to decrease feelings of inferiority and to give outlets for restlessness and hostility.

Generally, I prefer having elderly male and female patients working in a group together. This makes it possible to form attachments by visiting each other while working on their projects. It also tends to improve their personal habits. Sometimes such a close relationship leads to a marriage of an elderly couple after the end of the hospitalization and enhances motivation for leaving the hospital. The couples who do occupational therapy work together usually take a greater interest in recreational and outdoor activities, too, and the relationship between them helps their adjustment at the hospital remarkably.

Studying the application of occupational therapy for geriatric patients for many years has helped me to make the following observations: the preferred occupational therapy for men is woodworking—making waste baskets, doll furniture, magazine tables or end tables. The men also like to do weaving, link belts, rake knitting and plastic lace work, while the women prefer mending, crocheting, embroidery, piecing quilts, making doll clothes and sewing carpet strips. Both men and women enjoy gardening. The men do the heavy digging and clean the space for flowers; the women plant the seeds and take care of the ground; both are happy going out on the grounds and picking a bouquet.

The goal with occupational therapy in the geriatric group is essentially the same as with any other group of patients: elderly individuals need to gain self-esteem, become more self-confident, develop friendships and learn to express their aggressive drives in a socially acceptable and more controlled manner.

For increasing their self-esteem at the beginning of the treatment, simple projects should be started. Crafts used for this purpose may include waffle-weave mats, jersey loop potholders, wood burning and simple, easily completed wood projects such as doorstops, tie racks and small footstools. As soon as the geriatric patients are ready to try more difficult projects, the women may begin braid weaving on the upright loom or crocheting or making doll clothes. The men go on to more advanced woodworking which includes doll furniture, small tables, sawing, wastepaper baskets, fence pickets or a combination of these projects.

To improve social life, the men, for instance, were requested to make doll beds while the women prepared doll mattresses, sheets and pillowcases. Soon the patients started to discuss their projects together.

For a better outlet of aggressivity, clay work was used, and sawing wood, nailing the parts together, and some sanding were recommended. Tearing of rags appeared to be useful, too.

In the geriatric group, a special effort has to be made to improve the patients' memory and concentration. To increase their faculty to remember, it has been found useful to let the patients do simple, repetitive projects which require the same step over and over. To teach concentration, the project has to be one requiring full attention.

It is infrequent that geriatric patients get disturbed during occupational therapy sessions. Generally, they feel more satisfied, more needed and better accepted. I found it of value to have short sessions only, of no longer duration than one hour. Patients who have short attention spans should be encouraged to continue for a little longer than they may wish. The age of the patient, I observed, is not so great a handicap as the degree of physical disability.

It is, furthermore, of great importance that occupational therapy for geriatric patients should not consist of too minute or fine work. When planning projects for elderly patients, the individual's eyesight, physical handicaps and intelligence have to be taken into consideration. Geriatric patients usually need praise and encouragement.

A lasting and remarkable success for geriatric patients through occupational therapy is not easy to achieve. For the chronically ill patients it takes a longer period of time to respond to treatment because they have lost interest in their surroundings and often feel sorry for themselves. Acutely ill patients respond more quickly to treatment once they can be induced to start it, because their interest has not been interrupted for very long. They are usually more active and want to participate in a group.

The following case history might be helpful to illustrate how a confused, disoriented and hostile geriatric patient can be helped by skillful application of occupational therapy.

Case History

A 79-year-old patient was admitted to a psychiatric hospital. The reason for his admittance was that he wandered away from his home in the daytime, got lost on the streets and could not find his way back. He talked incoherently and became confused, was completely out of contact, was disoriented in all three spheres and became agitated at times. When placed in a nursing home he was aggressive toward other patients in the home, suffered from temper tantrums and, in fits of rage, destroyed furniture, tore bed sheets and his own clothing. He was brought to jail where he was put in restraint because of his destructive tendencies, and from jail he was finally transferred to the hospital for treatment.

At the hospital he was put on Thorazine® medication for a number of weeks and became quieter. His temper tantrums subsided in a couple of days and he was taken out of seclusion. Still completely out of contact, he talked in a rambling, confused and threatening manner to the aides and was taken out of his room to join an occupational therapy group of about twenty males and twenty females. At the beginning he refused to do any kind of work, threw wooden projects of other patients on the floor and ran away from the occupational therapy room.

I approached him daily, talked to him in very simple words about the occupational therapy tools and what could be done with them, encouraging him to try them. Again he refused and talked in a threatening way. He was spoken to for about ten days. Then one day he watched, with some interest, the work which one of the female patients was doing and said that she reminded him of his sister. The occupational therapy worker became attentive and let both of these patients sit together. After two more days, the patient volunteered to help to put some nails into a doll bed. The two patients finally started to get better acquainted. The next day, the patient wanted to help paint the doll bed. He was unable to handle the brushes, however. The occupational therapy worker helped him to do so in a friendly, encouraging way. When he finished the painting, the psychiatrist came and praised his work. The next day the patient smiled for the first time and, while continuing with his painting job, said some coherent words to the other patients and to the occupational therapist. The following day he asked to do a doll bed by himself, cutting the wood with a saw and putting the pieces together. The occupational therapist, anxious about giving the patient a saw and concerned about what he might do with it, asked the psychiatrist for advice. I agreed to the patient's wish, but together with the occupational therapist I watched carefully how the patient handled the tools. The patient did a perfect job and became more and more confident and talkative. He talked less confusedly, was friendlier and asked for more difficult jobs. He was put on a wooden sled project, building the sled and painting it, again, together with the female patient. He did an excellent job and was praised for it.

After six months this patient became oriented to time and place, talked coherently and was in good contact. He was friendly and cooperative, took part in all activities on the ward, liked to dance with "his sister" and showed much enjoyment in folk dances.

He participated in bingo games and offered a sled as a gift to the psychiatrist, with whom he talked about his interest in farming and carpenter work. He considered doing carpentry work at home to earn some money so that he could feel that "my family will be proud of me and will not consider me useless and too old to do anything." Then he stated that "if my wife does not know how many things I can do, I will take my sister home with me, and we will have a good time together."

This patient, who seemed to be, on arrival at the hospital, a "hopeless" case, was released from hospitalization after eight months.

Recreational Activities

No activity has been less understood and more abused than recreation. For many people recreational activities mean merely entertainment from which the patients get some enjoyment, like dancing, going to movies, watching television, hearing music on records or watching sports. For elderly persons, the proper approach to these activities is thought by some to be a more passive one because elderly individuals are believed to be physically unable or not mentally alert enough for active participation in recreational activities.

This approach appears to me to be ineffective. First of all, recreation never means entertainment, but a return to a creative life, salvage of something that has been lost or is in danger of being lost. It means, according to Gumpert,[200] restoration of, or the growth of, functions which have been abused or neglected in the routine of living. While work is a state of tension and leisure is characterized by a release from work-tension, meaningful relaxation is the necessary consequence of, and is conducive to, a new rhythmic flow of life which precedes, leads to and inspires creative work. If we lived in continuous tension—as many rigid and compulsive personalities do, without giving themselves time to relax, to experience leisure, to repose—the natural rhythm of life would be severely disturbed. No human being can remain physically and emotionally healthy by living in continuous tension but is in need of a recharge of his energies which restores the creative force in us. Life without relaxation would be monotonous and is a sign of becoming inflexible and more and more mechanical. Work done in this dull milieu is almost certain to be unimaginative and unoriginal. Humanity needs both work and relaxation to feel complete, just as it must experience the state of being awake and being asleep, day and night, stormy and calm waters of the ocean, like moonlight and sunshine, birth and death. We may call it the rhythm of life. When we disturb this rhythm artificially, we destroy nature around us and natural feelings in us.

To keep, to maintain, to restore the normal rhythm of life, compulsive human beings are in need of recreation. Therefore, recreational activities have a meaning, a purpose, a goal of great importance. For elderly persons, recreational activities are necessary and of value when they create an atmosphere of release from tension, of relaxation and when they "charge" them with new energy. Recreation can give a new direction to an older person's life and help him to find and to develop possibilities of emotional growth and intellectual understanding which the elderly individual has not dreamed of.

Recreational activities, therefore, are a means toward a well-defined goal. They should not be seen as technical procedures only but should be used individually and with skill to develop and maintain a new creative life. For this reason, it becomes necessary to understand the geriatric patients, to have a good knowledge of their assets and to learn about their hidden or forgotten talents and faculties, their unfulfilled wishes and intellectual desires, their motivation and their dreams. Like "Grandma" Moses, an elderly individual might be able to discover talents after the age of 70 and start a new, more complete, happier and more harmonious life.

According to Martin,[201] we are dealing in our everyday life mainly with what could be called "compulsive living" rather than "leisurely living." Compulsive intellectual preoccupation with one's internal problems is a characteristic symptom of many of our patients, young or old. "Creative insight," Hutchinson[202] pointed out, never occurred during the peak of mental effort but always during a period of relaxation. Relaxation, decrease of tension, and leisure are needed and achieved by recreational techniques which help us to return to a new, more creative life. Such recreational activities can be undertaken by watching a movie or television, by sport activity (hunting, fishing and others), hobbies (like stamp collecting), by reading books or magazines, gardening, planting flowers, caring for animals, sculpturing, working with clay, embroidery work, sewing, cooking, by wandering and observing nature (birds, animals, minerals) and many other activities. The recreational techniques to be used, with the purpose of relaxing the elderly patient, have to be chosen with great care and understanding of the elderly individual's assets, previous interests and limitations. These limitations can be as much of physical as of intellectual or emotional nature and should be evaluated by a competent recreational worker, with the help of a psychiatrist, before therapy is started. It is evident that very active athletic activities wherein the individual is forced and encouraged to compete with others are less suitable for most geriatric patients and might only induce greater tension and ruin our therapeutic goal. More passive activities might be indicated at times for the purpose of relaxation. Many elderly individuals, however, possess unknown qualities not discovered or not sufficiently used. Making it possible for them to use their assets and possibilities more purposefully and efficiently might help them to improve their emotional and physical health and restore them to many years of happy and creative life. According to W. Menninger,[203] the elderly person with a hobby is almost always an alert, interesting person. Recreation is an extremely important aid to growing older gracefully. People who stay young despite their years do so because of an active interest that provides satisfaction through participation.

Bortz,[204] in a very interesting paper, emphasizes that the problem of creative leisure will need to be studied, for work-related education is but one segment of our need. With higher standards of living and the new responsibility for citizens in today's challenging world, expanding leisure time will offer an opportunity, an unexcelled occasion for personal intellectual growth with broadening and deepening knowledge and understanding. This should be a basis in planning for adult education. In each child's life, a timetable should be set up for living a century-long lifetime of useful, happy and meaningful existence. In order to do this, it will be necessary to revise current attitudes toward aging.

Music Therapy

Music therapy for the geriatric patient appears to me a still-neglected but promising field which definitely has a place in his psychiatric treatment. I have found rhythm bands useful in awakening their interest in communication and socialization. Many geriatric patients found enjoyment in rhythm bands, started to participate with encouragement and sometimes showed a happy smile for the first time after many years. Music is an excellent means of arousing their interest and furthering their craving to belong. For example, playing a drum in an orchestra can help them to express and sublimate some of their hostility. Singing in a choir can stimulate their interest in religious participation and in other group activities. Finally, folk dances, for male and female patients in better contact with their environment, can help them to get not only better adjusted in the hospital but also to take interest in other persons and is of definite value to geriatric patients prior to their release from hospitalization when they return to community life or are placed in foster or old age homes where they meet persons of their own age and of the opposite sex. According to my experience, talking to members of the other sex, eating together with them in a dining room, and having recreational activities or dances with them are extremely necessary for geriatric patients who lived in a hospital environment for many years and have forgotten how to behave with members of the opposite sex in public.

According to Boxberger and Cotter,[205] participation in music activities had a beneficial effect on the behavior of geriatric patients. From the data the following results were noted: an increase in appropriate behavior, reduced aggression, less physical and verbal reaction to hallucinations, reduction of frequency in incontinency, improvement in personal appearance and a lowering of the level of undesirable patient noise. Geriatric patients need assistance to learn to grow old instead of merely becoming old. Music activities, according to the authors, assist in developing a more creative life, cultivating new interests, engaging in new activities, and re-establishing the necessary bonds with society.

Industrial Therapy

Industrial assignments have proved to be worthwhile for geriatric patients who need a goal and purpose in life and acceptance by the younger generation. Elderly patients, unless physically sick, can do many more things than we generally expect. With sufficient support they can often become conscientious clerks, gardeners, messengers or cooks in a psychiatric hospital and may often do well in a member-employee program. Sometimes they work with greater diligence and patience than younger patients.

The importance of an organized work therapy program has been emphasized in recent years especially by Mason.[206] He used a new work modality for geriatric patients, calling it "The Hospital Service Clinic" at the V.A. Hospital in Lexington, Kentucky. This clinic was furnished with work tables and tool storage equipment. It was under the supervision of the Manual Arts Therapy Section. There were geriatric patients with cardiac disease, hemiplegia and other chronic disabilities. An adequate work therapy program has been established with the goal of developing feelings of worth and confidence through accomplishment of meaningful tasks. Monetary incentive serves in this program as a powerful stimulus toward active participation.

Examples of work projects carried on in the clinic are as follows: assembling clinical folders for new admissions; processing worn clothing and linens into polishing and dust cloths; sorting and rolling socks; inserting carbons and stapling forms into sets; stamping forms and punching Acco fastener holes into specific forms; stuffing envelopes; pairing shoe laces; and assembling simple fabricated units such as lockers.

The finding that the span of attention increased markedly

when patients were engaged in meaningful and socially useful work activities is significant and should lead to reappraisal of the conditions under which clinical judgments regarding this symptom are derived.

Furthermore, Winick,[207] at the V.A. Hospital, Brockton, Massachusetts, developed a paid work program including elderly patients and is of the opinion that work brings meaning to people by its character-developing qualities. The individual in a work situation learns the meaning of assuming responsibility, punctuality, dedication, loyalty, obedience and honesty. He acquires knowledge and develops skills. With the development of competence a person feels more secure and confident. It is acceptance of the individual as a useful, reliable and knowledgeable person that is meaningful to him. Winick explains methods of evaluation by the psychiatric team for paid work assignment, the method for assignment of patients in regard to selection by an occupational, manual arts, educational or industrial therapist based on observation of patients' competence and attitude toward work. The third method for assignment is a request from the patient himself.

Educational Therapy

Educational therapy may be of value after careful consideration of the geriatric patient's assets and limitations. The discovery and utilization of hobbies and interests—for instance, reading books or magazines, learning a foreign language, participation in classes for accounting or typing—can be of value in the management of geriatric patients. During one of my psychiatric interviews, one 64-year-old male who was uncommunicative, listless and uninterested for more than twelve years of his hospitalization revealed interest in poetry and read to me a few poems he had written during the last year and kept carefully hidden in his pockets. He was praised and encouraged to write more poems, which were published in the hospital's patients' newspaper. From that time on the patient's emotional condition started to improve, slowly but constantly; he began to talk to other patients, became more interested in ward activities, lost his seclusive and shy attitude completely, and was considered for a release from hospitalization after seven months. The history of this patient is only one of very many known to me in which, by the intensive interest of the psychiatrist in, and an adequate utilization of a patient's assets, his mental condition improved considerably.

Educational therapy is especially useful for enhancing the self-esteem of elderly patients. Many of them get motivated to read books and magazines and to hold conferences on subjects of their own choice. A former lawyer, for instance, 66 years of age, was helped considerably in his treatment program by talking about economics and legal procedures to other patients and organized self-government of the patients on his ward. For him a carefully chosen educational program became an essential tool to leave the hospital and to adjust himself well in a foster home.

Physical Therapy and Hydrotherapy

Physical therapy and hydrotherapy have also been found of value for geriatric patients. According to Blustein,[208] electrical stimulation combined with Buerger-Allen exercises for circulatory disturbances in the lower extremities, general conditioning exercises using the stationary bicycle, individual exercises—especially posture exercises to prevent complications of inactivity—were used with success. According to my own experience, cold baths, scotch douches and active exercises, friction with cold water and general massage were frequently effective against symptoms of general weakness, fatigue and tiredness for elderly patients. However, all these techniques and exercises should be used only with caution and under constant supervision. Too much exercise and too-frequent hydrotherapeutic applications might be of damage to the geriatric patient. We should be aware of the fact that although we can use these techniques against the symptoms of fatigue successfully in some geriatric patients, they are no substitute for psychiatric treatment of the feelings of weakness and exhaustion which can be eliminated only when we are able to recognize the emotional factors involved and treat them accordingly.

Agitation and restlessness in geriatric patients can be treated successfully with warm baths or ¾ packs. For these special packs wet sheets are used covering the whole body up to the neck, leaving the upper extremities outside the pack. Immediately after the wet sheets of tepid temperature have been applied, a woolen blanket covers them completely and very closely to the body. These packs last not longer than ninety minutes, and the patient has to be observed continuously in regard to temperature, pulse and blood pressure.

Habit Training

Another factor of great concern is the geriatric patient's toilet habits. The more regressed a patient becomes, the worse his personal hygiene becomes. He might soil his clothing, not be able to control his urine or bowel function, show food particles on his shirt, burn his pants with cigarettes, remain unkempt, unshaved, and wash only when supervised. This deterioration of the geriatric patient's toilet habits increases with age and represents one of the symptoms of senility. To combat deterioration of toilet habits in elderly patients, a strict routine of washing, cleaning, changing beds, bathing the patients at regular hours, and a strict bedpan routine or the method of bringing the patients to the toilet at two-hour intervals in daytime and three-hour intervals at nighttime has been proved successful in some cases. However, according to my own experience, bedwetting of elderly patients represents, at times, not only a physical symptom of bladder weakness or paralysis but is used by the patient to express his anger, resentment and hostility because of his feelings of being neglected and not getting enough attention or loving care.

I believe that toilet training, too, has to be done by psychological means. When a geriatric patient feels secure and protected, when his feelings of resentment decrease, when he discontinues considering his ward nurse as an authoritative mother figure punishing him for his faulty habits and "pushing him around," or when he gets on friendly terms with the nursing personnel, the patient's toilet training improves remarkably.

Therefore, a rigid, authoritative routine cannot become a substitute for understanding, patience and loving attention. This appears to be the mistake of many toilet-training methods. Adequate training of the nursing personnel, who have to participate in the psychiatric program of rehabilitation of the geriatric patient, appears to be the only way of improving faulty toilet habits of the elderly when caused by emotional factors.

It is a fact that the successful therapy of the geriatric patient in a psychiatric institution should combine all these different methods and techniques of milieu therapy. Collaboration of the occupational therapy, recreational therapy and physical therapy departments is necessary. Only a combined, active and comprehensive program under the direction of a physician who knows the physical handicaps of his patients and the emotional factors involved in his patient's sickness can result in therapeutic success and, consequently, in rehabilitation.

VII

POST-HOSPITALIZATION CARE

THE DAY (OR NIGHT) HOSPITAL SYSTEM

IT IS GENERAL policy that no geriatric patient, once in remission from his psychosis or recovered from his confusion or disturbed behavior, should be permitted to leave the psychiatric institution without a plan for continuous treatment outside the hospital. If he has sufficient economic means, the best treatment is by his own family physician who has known the patient for many years prior to referring him to the psychiatric hospital. A letter of special recommendations, with a copy of the patient's psychiatric case record, should be in the private physician's hands before the patient returns to his home environment. The hospital psychiatrist has to explain the patient's psychodynamics and make understandable to the family doctor why and how the geriatric patient got disturbed, confused or psychotic, what kind of stress situation possibly caused his hospitalization and the patient's underlying personality structure. Furthermore, not only a diagnosis should be given but also a prognostic indication in regard to the possibility of future relapses of the patient, causing his eventual return to the hospital. Such a private and personal communication to the family physician should indicate, too, what medication (for instance, tranquilizers or energizers) have been given in the hospital with the exact dosage and, if possible, a recommendation by the psychiatrist that he wants the patient to continue his medication. The family physician should also be informed as to what other kind of psychiatric treatment has been given in the hospital—electrical shock treatment, for instance, individual or group psychotherapy, occupational, educational or recreational therapy, and others—so that the private physician might be able to continue with this treatment or change it as necessity arises according to his judgment and his own observations.

The danger of a relapse of the geriatric patient's emotional trouble is never greater than when a treatment is discontinued completely once the patient is released from hospitalization and then left to his own devices. At times the elderly patient returns to the same situation of stress or strain involving rejection by other members of his family, by his own children, by his spouse. They might not have been informed about the psychological causes of the patient's abnormal behavior and might go on treating him in a domineering way, belittling his efforts to remain active and creative or to find an adequate outlet in recreational activities or hobbies. They repeat the mistake of taking responsibilities from the elderly person which he is able to handle and further his regression due to lack of understanding. Therefore, a thorough explanation of the patient's emotional condition to his family physician and, through him, to other members of the patient's family, is necessary and indicated. Without this advice, the patient's return to hospitalization can be expected sooner or later. With adequate treatment at home, however, the geriatric patient's relapse into his emotional sickness can be avoided frequently.

In psychiatry, as in general medicine, the medical world becomes more and more aware of the fact that the patient's sickness should not be treated simply by treating the individual alone. All members of the family play an important role and, consciously or unconsciously, are a factor to be considered in regard to the origin, the recovery or the relapse of an individual's emotional sickness. Therefore, our goal in geriatric psychiatry is adequate treatment of the whole family or "the family constellation." This might involve interviews with the members of the family in the presence of the patient or without the patient being present. I believe that almost always our success or failure in psychiatric therapy depends upon our advice, recommendations or treatments given to the sick individual's relatives. We will have to understand that the disturbed interpersonal relationships are not the problem of the patient alone and that the patient is only part of his family. The family as a whole must be treated as it is recommended by Ackerman.[209] According to Ackerman, the individual is only a mirror image, a microcosm of his family group. The diagnosis of emotional illness and health cannot be restricted to the individual; it must encompass the individual within the group and the group as well. The ills of individuals, families and society are interrelated.

In case the patient has no family physician of his own or no means to afford a private doctor, the hospital psychiatrist still remains responsible for the patient's continuous observation and treatment after his release from the hospital. Adequate therapeutic methods have to be made continuously available in order to prevent relapses into the emotional sickness of the elderly patient.

There are many possibilities open to the psychiatrist from which to choose, according to the patient's mental condition and emotional needs. They are the day (or night) hospital system, the outpatient departments or mental hygiene clinics, the half-way houses, and the nursing homes. Of growing importance, too, are recreational day centers like the Sirovich Day Center or the Hodson Day Center in New York City or the Senior Citizens Center in San Francisco, which I consider to be of definite value for the maintenance of good emotional health among our Senior Citizens.

The idea of the day (or night) hospital is not a new one. Perhaps the oldest of this kind is at Gheel in Belgium. Well known also is the day hospital at the Allan Memorial Institute in Montreal, formerly under the direction of D. E. Cameron. and the day hospital of the Menninger Foundation in Topeka, Kansas. At the present time, many state and V.A. hospitals in the United States are using the day hospital system. In Europe, day hospitals have been emphasized, especially in Great Britain. While day hospitals in the United States have been built more for the purpose of posthospitalization care, in England many patients receive their initial treatment in day hospitals and are not necessarily hospitalized in full-time hospitals. At the Marlborough Day Hospital, modern psychopharmacological drugs and occupational activities are the treatment of choice, while at the Travistock Clinic, near London, individual psychotherapy is given extensively.

In England, the Cowley Road Hospital, which, under the direction of L. B. Cosin, is using the day hospital program with great success for geriatric patients, has become of great importance. To this day hospital report patients not in need of hospitalization who are treated with occupational therapy, physical therapy and an active retraining in the technique of social and daily living while living in their own homes. The emphasis is to avoid chronic hospitalization of geriatric patients. This new system has shown remarkable results.

According to Cosin,[210,211] a geriatric patient disturbed or confused or suffering from physical sickness of a more serious kind will be admitted immediately to the geriatric unit. Cosin thinks it is recommendable to treat the vicious circle of family anxiety stress increasing anxiety, depression and dementia in the old person. For patients unable to pay their own family doctor, the geriatric unit's social worker and doctor are responsible for his follow-up outside the hospital. Cosin also recommends intermittent readmission for summer holidays and at other times during the year when stress on the family group begins to increase, when the situation has been observed by the social worker. The geriatric patient is readmitted immediately to the geriatric unit in the event of serious illness affecting the elderly patient or other members of the family group. Cosin emphasizes maintenance of optimal emotional and physical health for the geriatric patient by utilizing physical medicine and occupational therapy with a very active approach, while group psychotherapy is used at the Oxford Unit only to a minor degree. All geriatric patients with emotional disturbances are treated, however, by a psychiatrist.

According to Cosin, about 25 per cent of one thousand patients admitted yearly suffer from severe mental disturbance, and 11 per cent, or about one hundred a year, have had long-standing emotional disturbances. About 38 per cent of these one hundred patients are eventually discharged to their homes;

7 per cent are resettled in private nursing homes or long-stay annexes. Seventeen per cent die of intercurrent infection, 9 per cent are "certified" and transferred to mental hospitals. Only 19 per cent generally remain residents at the Oxford Unit four to ten months after admission. Three-quarters of the discharged patients attend the day hospital from one to five days a week and are helped to stay outside the hospital by this means. Very few of the day hospital patients need emergency readmission. The average age of the patients treated at the Oxford Day Hospital is 78 years.

Many hospitals in the United States now are using the system of day hospitals but some of them also include the night hospital method which permits patients to get treatment after working hours. They are permitted to sleep in the hospital and receive treatment more suitable for them when already employed but still in need of support.

There is no doubt that the idea of the day and night hospital has great promises for the future, especially for patients in the older age group, and needs to be developed further.

As Polner[212] has pointed out, the advantages of the day hospital for geriatric patients is not only of economic nature because the total cost per day is considerably less than the cost of hospitalization in an inpatient facility but also the greatest advantages lies in the fact that the patient keeps his place in the family and support is given not only to the patient but also to other members of the patient's family, relieving them from many anxieties and making it possible for them to work during the time the patient is at the day hospital. However, according to Polner, possible disadvantages in the day hospital program might result from the fact that the home environment is not always the most suitable for the patient and might undo some of the therapeutic work done with and for the patient at the hospital. Another aged person might also impose great strain on other members of the family at home. In the United States, in contrast to Great Britain, Canada, and some European countries, the day hospital program is recommended for indigent patients only, while the private physician's responsibilities are stressed. It is felt here that more benefit can be derived in training the general practitioner himself to treat more effectively his geriatric patients after hospitalization. However, in cases where the day hospital treatment is economically and psychologically indicated, the intensive and competent treatment of the day and night hospital program with a minimum disruption of family life and community living is a necessity and of great importance for our geriatric patient population.

Anderson[213] and co-workers made an interesting study at St. Elisabeth's Hospital in Washington, D.C. and found out that after six months the patients under 70 years of age with primarily functional symptoms and in relatively good physical condition are likely to have returned to the community. Patients over 80 years of age, severely disturbed and in very poor physical condition, may have died. If we are to reduce the geriatric mental population we shall need to concentrate on patients of 70 or above, manifesting, in varying degrees, problems of comprehension, orientation, and physical and social adjustment to the environment. Fifty patients 64 years of age or over, entering the Geriatric Division of St. Elisabeth's Hospital from March 1, 1963 to September 1, 1963, were screened.

At the present, many large cities have such day hospitals in the United States as well as in Western Europe. They are in close affiliation with clinics and hospitals. During the last few years, the idea of the day hospital and its usefulness has grown, and many day hospitals have been built in connection with state mental hospitals and V.A. hospitals, where young and older patients are observed and treated under the supervision of psychiatrists or a psychiatric team which might include also a psychologist, a social worker, and an occupational therapist or recreation specialist. Also, in some of these day hospitals, geriatric patients released from hospitalization are treated by individual and group psychotherapy and take part in many occupational or recreational activities. In this way, the geriatric patient (as are children, young adults and middle-aged persons of both sexes) is treated according to his needs and therefore relapses into a psychotic condition are frequently prevented.

NURSING HOME CARE

In the United States, half of the nursing homes are proprietary, while the others belong to state or federal governments, church organizations, or other private charity organizations. It is evident that the number of aged persons over 65 in nursing homes is increasing in proportion to a general increase of the aging population. Although many states have enforced rigid standards for nursing home care and supervision which requires medical treatment, adequate nursing care and equipment, including standards for bed space, fire prevention, bathing facilities, kitchen hygiene and others, there are still, unfortunately, "old-age homes" or "boarding homes" which are not at the level of the licensed nursing homes and should be eliminated. The duties and responsibilities of the nursing home administrator which are various and difficult have been outlined by Kaplan,[214] Director of the Mansfield Memorial Homes, Inc., in Ohio. These duties include having a thorough knowledge and understanding of the basic concepts, philosophy and current trends in gerontology; interpreting problems of the aged to special publics when requested; and utilizing the modern principles of public, social welfare, hospital and business administration. Most important, however, in addition to providing for adequate shelter, hygienic methods, nursing care, medical treatment when it becomes necessary, individualized meals according to dietary and other requirements of the older generation, the nursing home administrator must be able to understand the emotional needs of his clients. He has to keep them in contact with the community aspect of life, furnish adequate recreational and occupational activities in the home, encourage all' kinds of hobbies, fulfill the elderly person's religious interests, and keep a good balance between the elderly citizen's wanting to "disengage himself" at times from the outside world and remain in a desired state of "individual separation," and the same person's cravings, at other times, toward human contact, to socialize, to play games with others and to share activities.

Savitz[215] points out that a person admitted to a home for

the aged should be provided with all possible safety measures and with medical care by an adequate, properly trained medical staff who work as a team with understanding and sympathy. The personality and the individuality of the aged resident must be respected, and this should be reflected in his care and environment. The four phases of the medical program—preventive, curative, rehabilitative and environmental—plus auxiliary services, combine to add life and pleasure to the old person's added years and to make these years more meaningful.

Dominick and co-workers[216] at the Boston State Hospital have made a special study recently in regard to the adjustment of elderly patients in nursing homes and found that successfully adjusted patients were found better prepared in advance for placement in the home, more active, enjoying better interpersonal relations with roommates and others. Nevertheless, there was a great need for increased communciation by nurses with patients and initiation of more activities for patients in nursing homes.

Linn and Gurel[217] observed the initial reaction of patients in nursing homes and stated that if during the first week of placement the patient's condition remains fairly stable, there is still time to build on these strengths for purposes of rehabilitation whenever possible.

Stotsky[218] described the exacerbation of psychiatric symptoms in determining the outcome of nursing home placement and came to the conclusion that poor relationships with the family and social adjustment were also of significance. The physical and social characteristics of the nursing home—presence or absence of recreational and rehabilitative facilities, the type of medical facilities—and the home's relationship with the community were not related to the outcome.

He also found that institutional deprivation may be physical, intellectual or spiritual. Deprivation in nursing homes was found to be particularly related to (1) lack of stimulation, (2) lack of adequate walking space inside and outside the homes, (3) lack of recreational and occupational therapy, (4) lack of space for group socialization and activities, (5) lack of common dining room, so that patients have to eat off trays in their rooms, (6) absence of volunteer workers from the community, (7) separation of patients on different floors and (8) minimal socialization between male and female patients.

Proposed programs for overcoming these problems include (1) in-service training of staff, (2) better communication between the state hospital and the nursing home, (3) intervention for emergencies or recurring problems, (4) the establishment of recreational and occupational therapy, and (5) the recruitment of volunteers to visit, conduct group games and arrange extramural activities.

Goldfarb,[219] who has great experience in treating geriatric patients in nursing homes, made the following predictions in regard to mortality in the aged in a seven-year follow-up study: severe brain syndrome, incontinence, and physical dependence more readily predict limited life expectancy than age or physician's opinion. Death rate is more closely related to these conditions than to the type of institutional residence.

Of great importance appears to be the elderly individual's attitude toward members of his own family, his children and grandchildren. Elderly persons do not want to be considered a burden by members of their own family belonging to the younger generation, and at times put on a mask of wanting to stay aloof and isolated. Frequently, however, behind their air of aloofness, the need to meet their own children and grandchildren is very great, and they actually become alive and happy again in their company. At other times, when bothered by the physical ailments, so frequent in elderly people, they do want to be alone and do not wish their children or grandchildren to know about these matters. Not infrequently, elderly persons need relatively more time for sleep and rest; they tire more easily and show features of fatigue. Therefore, the time element of visits with the younger generation is for them of great importance. Visits of too long duration might be resented by elderly citizens. Elderly individuals also are much in need of "meditation." They like to think about problems which are different from the ones of the younger generation. They have other ideas about "life" and the many activities in which young people are interested. They might not be able to understand some of the cravings and ambitions of the younger generation in a changing world.

Therefore, a certain equilibrium between the elderly person's passive meditative attitude, conducive to disengagement and wanted isolation, and his wish to participate in the life of younger people and feel part of their group is, according to my own experience with elderly people, a very important factor in handling them and keeping them happy and satisfied in nursing homes as well as in psychiatric institutions. A nursing home administrator, aware of these problems and able to handle them with tact and diplomacy, will surely contribute a great deal to the adjustment in the home and to the upholding of his clients' emotional equilibrium, his mental as well as physical health.

Whenever the elderly person gets emotionally disturbed or greatly confused or suffers from a physical sickness of a serious degree, transfer to a psychiatric institution or a general hospital might become a necessity. Therefore, no nursing home should be permitted to function without a psychiatric consultation service and adequate medical supervision, for the benefit and protection of the nursing home administrator as well as for the elderly clients.

I am very much in agreement with Leeds,[220] who emphasizes that we find ourselves in a period of evolution of the home for the aged. The administrators of homes for the aged should act as an educational force and build close relationships with other medical facilities. The future home for the aged will be a complex geriatric facility that combines both medical care and fulfills the elderly citizen's needs for social, religious, recreational and occupational activities.

For this reason, in 1957, under my direction, in a state hospital in Kansas, special training courses of four days' duration were given for nursing home administrators. They visited the state hospital and took part in lectures and seminars about geriatric psychiatry and observed on the geriatric wards the modern psychiatric treatment methods for elderly patients. In this way, the nursing home administrators not only bettered their knowledge and skill, but the relationships between the psychiatric hospital and the nursing homes were improved. Furthermore, through better communication, the continuation of the geriatric patient's treatment after release from the hospital and transfer to a nursing home was furthered. Such a program is of definite value and should be introduced in all psychiatric institutions treating geriatric patients.

DAY CARE CENTERS

The treatment of the geriatric patient furthermore would be incomplete and unsatisfactory without the cooperation of a suitable day care center.

New York City has many excellently organized day care centers sponsored by the Department of Welfare, the best known of which are the Hodson Center (founded 1943) and the Sirovich Day Center (opened 1949). They are usually open five days a week, admit elderly citizens of both sexes and without discrimination, have psychiatric and medical consultants and are under the direction of a trained social worker. In these centers the older person fills his unused day with activity that will stimulate and reactivate his hobbies, interests, assets and experiences and give him a feeling of accomplishment and usefulness. In these day centers the elderly persons work and play; they have their own hobby shops, do carpenter work, repair radios and television sets, build their own furniture, cook their own meals, mend their clothing, wash their laundry, paint pictures, study languages, learn or play musical instruments, singly or as an orchestra, meet in discussion groups, read books and magazines, have their own entertainment and even have their own poetry club where the elderly citizen reads and writes his own poetry. According to Levine,[221] consultant to and founder of the Hodson Center in New York City, activity for the older person is as essential to life as is food and shelter. Vegetating for the elderly is a form of deterioration and regression, leading to institutionalization and to slow death. A balanced program, taking into consideration his physical and emotional condition, can renew old interests and find new opportunities. In such a day center the elderly individual can meet people and make new friends and regain his feeling of belonging to a group. Group work programs are created, and group activities are developed. Active participation and social activities are enhanced, and the elderly citizen learns again to carry responsibilities and gains new goals in life. Realistic attitudes toward life in general are assumed, and many new skills are learned which help later in gainful employment, if so desired. These day centers for elderly persons over 60 are valuable and useful institutions of our modern culture and are helpful in preventing emotional disturbances of the elderly by maintenance of their self-esteem and by letting them feel wanted, needed and accepted. When an elderly individual gets disturbed or confused, medical and psychiatric help is requested, frequently preventing hospitalization in a psychiatric institution.

There is no doubt that some of these day centers still suffer from lack of adequate personnel and equipment, but the idea of the day center is of value and should be developed further in the future.

According to Kubie and Landau,[222] self-government is emphasized in day centers because the institution of self-government has proved to be one of the effective means of stimulating these older people to make use of their individual capacities. It has developed leadership, initiative, responsibility. It has also served to focus attention on, and increase identification with, the affairs of the center, even among the least participating members.

HALF-WAY HOUSES, FOSTER HOMES AND COMMUNITY ACTIVITIES

Of growing importance for the rehabilitation of the geriatric patients who are not able to return to their own family is the utilization of other community resources. Such programs involve placement in private families (foster homes); help with planning for suitable living arrangements in the community, residence hotels or apartment projects; meals-on-wheels; "friendly visitor" services by Red Cross or volunteer groups; voluntary recreational facilities in the community such as Golden Age or Senior Citizens Clubs; vocational guidance; placement in sheltered workshops; and legal guardianship service. In England and in Australia, the "meals-on-wheels" service is emphasized because the philosophy behind such a service is that, frequently, elderly persons are not able to leave their own home owing to physical sickness or emotional resistance and anxiety about meeting other people, or shame because of their condition. Furthermore, its value is enhanced by the fact that the "meals-on-wheels" program releases the elderly individual from the duties of preparing his own meal and permits him more time for recreational, occupational and other activities which would enhance his emotional and physical health. Such a service might also make it possible to release geriatric patients earlier from hospitalization. All these home services for elderly individuals should not take the initiative from the patient. They should not work against the geriatric patient's personal drive, ambition and motivation and should not make life too easy for him and, eventually, further his regression.

At the 7th International Congress on Mental Health in London, England, August 1968, Fendell[223] described a new role for foster grandparents. Impoverished senior citizens became foster parents to the mentally retarded, earning needed income for themselves, and the young retardates received the loving, individualized attention they so desperately need and responded by giving the elderly foster grandparents the sense of worth activity, of being needed.

At-home nursing, organized on a municipal or federal basis, may become a necessity for geriatric patients who are not in need of full-time nursing care and supervision in a nursing home and do not have financial means to provide these services on their own.

Daniels and Kahn,[224] too, emphasize special services as needed: "meals-on-wheels," special residential facilities and home visitation. Medicare and community mental health are potent forces to stimulate the development for more comprehensive services for the aged and are the responsibility of the catch-ment area.

So called half-way houses finally are becoming an increasing necessity. Such half-way houses represent a useful facility for geriatric patients who do not have a home or a family of their own and cannot be placed in a foster home but are not in need of a psychiatric treatment program in a hospital or of continuous nursing care and supervision in a nursing home. The patients in this group work in the community during the day but return after their working hours to the protective environment of a half-way house which is under the direction of a social worker, a nurse or a similarly experienced individual in the field of gerontology who is able to give the elderly individual support when needed. Such a half-way house contains a greater number of patients than a foster home and has a closer communication system with the hospital from which the patients were released. This system of half-way houses, used extensively in England and gaining popularity in the United States, appears to be of usefulness for elderly patients who are not yet able to stand completely on their own feet and who are in need of support to find or hold a job, but who definitely do not require hospitalization any more.

The different types of programs concerned with the geriatric patient's emotional and physical health are many and vary according to the patient's needs. Therefore, skill, knowledge and flexibility are of the greatest importance to the psychiatrist, who still shares the responsibility for the patient after his release from hospitalization. For this purpose, he has to utilize, on a highly individualized basis, not only the services of the patient's family physician but also the many services which the community has to offer. Therefore, a closer cooperation with the community and its organizations, which have to do things "with but not *for* the geriatric patients," is the proper approach to the solution of the continuously growing problem of our elderly individuals.

FAMILY THERAPY

Family therapy for geriatric patients is still a neglected field of treatment for the elderly and should be emphasized much more. At the Fort Logan Mental Health Center in Denver (Colorado) a very successful family therapy has been used for years.[225] The psychiatrist, together with the social worker, meets the family members of the geriatric patient once weekly and discusses in the presence of the patients their most important concerns and conflicts. In this way the discharge rate of the elderly who are hospitalized at the Center is greatly enhanced. In an interesting paper, Miller[226] confirms these observations and states that the study of the chronically ill aged person provides special opportunities to observe patient-family interactions. Such observations contribute to the study of comprehensive care. Miller recommends that the medical focus should be expanded to include the family in the treatment unit. It is necessary that the physician become more oriented toward the impact of the patient's illness on the immediate and remote social environment (and vice versa). The medical profession should learn to work in symbiotic association with its sister social sciences—sociology, pyschology, anthropology and theology. Treatment of the patient as a whole person includes the study and management of the family as an entity, as has been described and emphasized by Jones,[227] Ackerman,[228] Liebman,[229] Wolff[230] and others.

VIII

OUR GOAL: FROM CUSTODIAL CARE TOWARD REHABILITATION

In some psychiatric institutions we still find the elderly patient sitting with hopelessness and depression on his face, uninterested in his surroundings, listless, apathetic, and at times, even neglected in his personal appearance—unkempt, unshaved, sloppy with his clothing, and more or less out of contact or mute. These patients convey the feeling of being outcasts of a society which does not care if they live or die, believing at times that "they would be better off dead" because "nothing can be done for them." They are "just old people waiting to die."

Fortunately, this "ward atmosphere" is slowly disappearing and is being replaced more and more by greater activity among the patients and an increasing interest by personnel in them. On many wards we find recreational activities such as card playing, table tennis, checkers, chess, television, radio music and occasional dances organized by volunteers or recreational workers. Nonetheless, the general attitude of the ward physician, nursing personnel, and the rest of the psychiatric team frequently remains one of hopelessness and depression and not being able to understand the whole situation or to do something about it.

What are the reasons for this neglect? In regard to the psychiatrists, they frequently feel that elderly people are not approachable by psychotherapy because of their confusion, memory defects and delusional behavior. Others make an initial effort but find it difficult to have empathy with the elderly, lose patience and so then become discouraged because of their lack of success. Occasionally an elderly physician identifies with a geriatric patient but becomes depressed himself, especially if the elderly patient suffered from a heart condition or other physical ailment which the physician himself being of the same age, is afraid of developing. Other physicians become definitely hostile toward the geriatric patient because they are themselves deeply involved in an unresolved Oedipus complex. They may treat the female patient—if they themselves belong to the male sex—with great preference, sympathy and overindulgence, while the male geriatric patients are neglected or treated with too great strictness and control because they remind them of their own father. They become unconsciously vindictive and act out their resentment against their own father by unconsciously hating the patient. With the female physician, the roles may be reversed, but the underlying hostility sometimes comes into the open by threatening the patient with electric shock treatment or by taking their privileges away from them.

Therefore, it is of utmost importance in the treatment of the geriatric patient for the therapist to have an empathetic, understanding, supportive and loving attitude, together with objectivity and a mind open to understanding the patient's problems. Also harmful is the tendency to slap the patient on the back, show pity and take away from him his responsibilities and his maturity. Elderly patients often act like children and overemphasize their helplessness in bathing, dressing or feeding. Nothing would be more incorrect than doing too much for them. It would only intensify their attitude of unresponsible helplessness, apathy and undignified dependency.

Another important problem to be kept in mind continuously when treating an elderly patient is the physician's and the patient's attitude toward old age generally and death particularly. Any person who is afraid of getting old and finds it depressing and fearful, any individual who is afraid to die and clings desperately to the delusion of his youthfulness will not be able to treat elderly patients successfully. A realistic philosophy toward life and death based on the inevitability of growing old and dying and on the belief that death is part of living and basic to its fulfillment is necessary in helping geriatric patients.

Religion might be of assistance in overcoming the fear of dying. When a person's life has found full satisfaction—by creating a family or piece of art, by contributing to science, or indeed by creating anything of use, enjoyment, of purposeful advancement for other people, a community or a country—death should not be a cause of fear but of meaningful rest, giving others a chance and a possibility to grow, to develop and to further one's own creation. When the psychiatrist is able to feel this way and convey his calm and his hope by having overcome his own fear of death, when he himself has understood the full meaning of life, of growth and of sharing with others, when he is convinced that the younger generation has to develop its own creative efforts after careful consideration of what has been built by the older generation in the past—only then will the psychiatrist or the physician who treats the elderly have the possibility to understand them deeply and to show them the way out of emotional conflicts and worry and the way toward freedom, calm and serenity.

The goal of "successful aging," according to Havighurst,[231] should not be occasioned with only one particular life-style, whether it be one of activity or one of disengagement. Life satisfaction will probably be associated with active involvement for some kinds of people. For others, disengagement will be the source of adjustment.

There is no simple theory of successful aging which can account for all the people in their later years. There is some disengaging force to withdraw from society in some persons over 70 or 80. But most of them will retain the attitude toward life of their middle years. Those who were happy and satisfied in their activity and productivity will then continue to be happy and satisfied if they can maintain a considerable part of their activity and productiveness. Those who were happy and satisfied by being relatively passive and dependent in their middle years will be happy and satisfied if they can become even more disengaged in their later years.

Therefore, the problem of rehabilitation is not a simple one. It can be handled only on an individual basis. There are a few definite needs, however, which must be fulfilled if a human being is to remain emotionally healthy and not succumb to the many conflicts, abnormal reactions and moods accompanying the process of aging. The most outstanding needs which bring unhappiness, dissatisfaction and emotional ill health when not satisfied are of a physiological nature involving body-growth, nourishment and organ function and of psychological nature—the need to feel safe from danger and threat, to belong to a group and to be loved, the need for prestige and recognition, for self-actualization and, for some persons, for aesthetic surroundings and for beauty.

The geriatric patient has lost many of his satisfactions; he considers himself "lost," without purpose, without goal, without direction. He is confused, believes himself frequently to be a burden and realizes, consciously or unconsciously, that life has no more meaning for him.

A rehabilitation program, therefore, should take into consideration the geriatric patient's present physical and mental condition in an objective and highly individualized way. It has to improve upon his physical condition and disabilities by means of all the scientific methods and treatments available to modern medicine, restoring, if possible, to the elderly patient's physical condition the physical strength and vigor of his former adult life, using physical therapy, hydrotherapy, drugs, diet, and corrective therapy when indicated. But such a rehabilitation program must give greatest importance to the emotional problem involved in order to restore a patient not only to his previous physical state of health but also to emotional equilibrium.

An excellent rehabilitation service for the elderly patient has been practiced for many years at the Geriatric Center in Oxford, England, by Cosin,[232] who has classified geriatric rehabilitation into three categories: (1) idiopathic rehabilitation—the restoration of function following a disability that results from a major pathological process (fractured femur, hemiplegia or rheumatoid arthritis); (2) heteropathic rehabilitation—a general restoration of activity despite a pathological process affecting the efficiency of the body as a whole; and (3) combined heteropathic and idiopathic rehabilitation.

Similarly, Rusk and Dasco,[233] well known as pioneers for rehabilitation of the handicapped have classified the rehabilitation of old people into three groups: (1) restoration of the obviously handicapped patient (hemiplegia, fractures, amputations, neuromuscular diseases); (2) restoration of the chronically ill person who has no signs of manifest disability (chronic cardiac disease); (3) restoration of the elderly person who is not obviously ill but whose physical fitness is impaired.

The importance of rehabilitation instead of bed rest has been emphasized by Bonner[234] at the Cardinal Cushing Rehabilitation Center, Cambridge, Massachusetts. According to this author, bed rest even for only a few weeks is a most dangerous thing for an older person to experience. Physical activity is vital, not only to prevent disability but in many instances to preserve life itself.

Knudson[235] advises that this type of health promotion would include rehabilitation techniques for the prevention of illness and disability, with the objective of halting impairment of health and onset of disability. The psychiatrist, with his rehabilitation team, should contribute a part of the total resources brought to bear in an aggressive approach in such a preventive program. Prior to any treatment program, a comprehensive health inventory should be made for each individual. Physical medicine and rehabilitation, according to Knudson, can be of real help in prevocational activities in determining and increasing work capacity, physical tolerance, mental alertness and emotional stability.

Braceland[236] is of the opinion that psychiatry and rehabilitation deal with two of the greatest adversities that befall mankind: mental and physical disaster, whether innate or acquired, acute or chronic, temporary or prolonged. They both work in the framework of the therapeutic environment and the therapeutic team and thus in the context of group dynamics. They deal with an individual who lives, feels, thinks, struggles, and expends his energy in defending himself against a threat to his integrity. Therefore, psychiatry and rehabilitation have to re-habilitate man *as man,* no matter how badly disabled he may be or how seriously restricted his activities are. The patient has to return to society a "complete person," skilled or perhaps new-ly skilled in important techniques and especially in the art of living. A revision of his "body image" might become necessary; his conception of himself and of his relations to others might have to be changed. For this purpose, the psychiatrist will have to work with the more mature aspects of the patient's person-ality in order to prevent chronic regression and lasting disability.

An adequate rehabilitation service for the geriatric patient therefore includes: restoration of his physical health and pre-vention of further physical disabilities by corrective and pre-ventive treatment in an institution well equipped for this pur-pose, and keeping the elderly patient in good emotional equili-brium by all means available to the psychiatrist or well-trained physician.

Timm,[237] in an interesting paper, emphasizes that an effec-tive psychiatric program for geriatric patients will insure that no correctable physical defect is overlooked or untreated; anxi-ety levels will be reduced; psychiatric therapies to meet specific needs will be applied as in any age group; and an activity pro-gram will be designed around the individual patient to restore his interest in others and to give meaning to his life. The pro-gram also should include comprehensive discharge planning so that the patient can be returned to his home at the earliest possible time. This requires careful work and counseling with families or friends and full utilization of community agencies and organizations.

Busse and co-workers[238] found that elderly patients who continued to work beyond their usual age of retirement had a higher intellectual capacity than those who did not. They also suffered less from depression. Of 73 subjects whose sensorium remained intact and who maintained their usual personality integration were occupied in some form of useful activity which brought them into contact with others. These investigators sug-gest that this continuing activity may be an important factor in the maintenance of a clear sensorium and successful adaptation to aging.

Davis[239] believes that activity therapy serves as a concept of challenge, represents a motivational tool associated with rewards, while Filer and O'Connell[240] emphasize that many hospitalized and convalescent older persons are living at a minimal level of performance and are capable of much better functioning if the right conditions are provided. They also emphasize the importance of rewards and of setting goals for conduct in the rehabilitation of older persons.

Folsom,[241] at the V.A. Hospital, Tuscaloosa, Alabama, recommends a special attitude therapy for geriatric patients. The following "attitudes" are recommended: (1) "kind firmness" and insistence upon ungratifying work from the depressed patient; (2) a "matter of fact" attitude for alcoholics and character disorders generally; (3) "active friendliness" for withdrawn and apathetic patients; (4) "passive friendliness" for paranoid patients with latent homosexual problems; and (5) "no demand" for those patients with "genuine rages."

This attitude therapy has been used extensively in a geriatric reorientation unit. The patients, according to Folsom, responded well by taking part in activities off the unit. Many were able to follow a self-care program. Patients considered confused and hopeless made progress. This program is successful, Folsom reports, because the entire staff is active, optimistic, and rehabilitation-oriented. The danger, however, is, I believe, that these therapeutic attitudes might become therapeutic stereotypes, whereby patients are not treated as individuals with their own specific problems, evaluated carefully and treated on an individual basis. Oversimplification, according to my experience, should be avoided especially in regard to depressed and suicidal geriatric patients, as has been pointed out by the author.[242]

In a growing number of psychiatric institutions conditioning therapies have been used with advantage. Cohen[243] states that the conditioning therapies are successfully applying learning theory and methodology to many complex behavior problems, while Reyna[244] predicts that more rigorous application of laws of learning will make conditional therapies even more effective and will extend their use to a broader range of behavior problems. It is hoped that this will include the geriatric population which definitely requires carefully worked out process and outcome studies. Such studies can help (1) evaluate the effectiveness of conditioning therapies when applied to persons whose behavior problems involve psychophysiological, somatic, and/or neurological deficits; (2) work out the relationship between age and conditioning which is, as yet, far from clear; (3) determine in the geriatric population the relationship between conditionability, intelligence, and neurological impairments. Revusky[245] and co-workers studied automated training of social relationships with extremely withdrawn geriatric patients and felt that this type of training might be a substitute for milieu therapy.

Goldfarb[246] thinks that the geriatric patient's dependency needs frequently present a great obstacle in the rehabilitation process. With increasing age, added socioeconomic losses and continued physical or mental decline of the individual, sociomedical opportunity to exert corrective action is generally decreased. One exception is the continuing opportunity to respond appropriately to the irrational aspect of the patient's search for aid: his dependency. Professional awareness and judicious acceptance of the patient's dependency leads to diminution of its overt manifestations, to increased self-sufficient behavior, and quasi-independent action.

Simon,[247] studying the practical application of rehabilitation techniques at the Langley Porter Neuropsychiatric Institute in San Francisco, comes to the conclusion that current concepts of aging have lagged behind the often spectacular progress of other fields of medicine in recent decades. Fortunately, society is beginning to look at the aged from a new perspective, to recognize their right to have the resources of the community mobilized in their behalf. The need is great for reliable information about the incidence and prevalence of disability in the elderly, the effectiveness of various preventive, treatment and rehabilitation programs, and the most efficient and helpful ways of providing needed services to the elderly population.

Korson,[248] at the Mental Health Institute in Independence, Iowa, has made the following observations: Patients over 65 were admitted directly to the geriatric unit. In one area patients received intensive psychiatric treatment (group and individual therapy, ward government, remotivation techniques, occupational therapy and other activity therapies such as music, recreation, adult education and homemaking services, as well as intensive casework by experienced social workers). In the second area were the patients who were markedly regressed. When they showed improvement, they were transferred to the first unit. Under the new regimen, the discharge rate for geriatric patients increased from 36 per cent to 59 per cent, and the discharge rate to their homes from 28 per cent to 47 per cent. The average length of stay in the hospital was markedly reduced from 112 days to 65 days.

Kobrynski[249] (Regina, Saskatchewan, Canada) points out that the concept of the "whole patient" applies more to the aged than to any other group; his assets and liabilities of all systems must be carefully evaluated. The goal of geriatric rehabilitation is restoration of ability for self-care and especially the restoration or improvement of ambulatory capacity. The therapeutic program applied in rehabilitation of an elderly patient includes (1) medical treatment of the multiple pathologic conditions common in the elderly and (2) special therapies necessary for the improvement of function. Rehabilitation is a team effort which involves many professional people: doctors, nurses, physiotherapists, occupational therapists, speech therapists and social workers. Medical, psychologic and social factors must be considered. Communities, governments and medical societies must find a way to facilitate the task of the individual doctor in the management of the elderly patient, through provision of facilities, ancillary staff and programs of postgraduate education in geriatric care.

Many patients subjected to prolonged bed rest undergo progressive intellectual and emotional as well as physical deterioration. Sensory deprivation and forced dependency favors the development of increasing dependency, loss of personal sense of worth and depression. Rehabilitation techniques especially necessary for patients suffering from decreased muscle tone (atrophy), contractures, circulatory disturbances, decubitus ulcers, urinary bladder dysfunction, bowel dysfunction and respiratory problems. Bed pans are used only during night shifts. At all other times all patients are mobilized out of bed to the toilet for bowel movements.

The goal and purpose of the rehabilitation program for the geriatric patient is, therefore, to restore and keep his physical strength and vigor, to help him regain his emotional equilibrium, disturbed by the factor of aging, and return him to the circle of his family and his community as a dignified and creative human being whose needs to be loved, accepted in and by a group, to feel needed and to have a high self-esteem are satisfied. The aged patient has to become again part of humanity, adjusted as well as possible to the problems of a progressive world, with faith in himself, in his future and in others.

No real rehabilitation of the geriatric patient, however, is possible, I believe, unless the fear to die, present on a conscious or unconscious level in nearly all elderly persons, can be overcome. It is quite evident that the psychiatrist, in his therapeutic approach to the geriatric patient, has to be aware of the attitudes that elderly patients reveal about death and dying, of their own image of aging, of their goals and values in life, and of their dependency needs. Most people in our culture have great difficulty accepting aging as a natural process without feelings of resentment or inferiority. The psychiatrist must help them realize that they can compensate for their decline in physical attractiveness by giving greater value to the intellectual and emotional factors of their life's experiences and by developing patience and wisdom; he must help them not to consider decrease in sexual potency and physical strength as completely negative, but instead to sublimate those energies by redirecting their free-floating libido to contemplation, cultural achievement, or religious activities. Many elderly people can find new values and interest for which they had no time in earlier years. Grandma Moses, who began to paint when she was over 70, is a model for that kind of achievement.

However, we must change the image of aging not only in the elderly themselves but in our whole society. As long as our American culture is predominantly youth-directed, setting fast and compulsive work and economic success as our highest goals, we can do justice neither to our older nor to our younger generations. I have observed that many persons in their later years come to perceive these very attitudes, which they themselves had held all their lives, as faulty, unworthy, and actually destructive. They seek assistance in achieving different values and goals, and we must help them to work through the process of re-evaluation. We have much to learn from the elderly as they work to change their lifelong philosophies and values.

The physician has to handle the fear of dying and death in the elderly with special care and circumspection. Timing is very important. Too many therapists ignore the issue or try surreptitiously to delay dealing with the problems. A clergyman might help some people face this overwhelming problem; the promise of a better life after death might persuade some to feel less disturbed. However, it has been my experience that more important than the idea of life hereafter to the patient's adjustment is his belief that he has not lived and is not now living in vain. Such a belief often leads to his feeling calm and serene. He can benefit from being told, sincerely, that he has accomplished important things in life, such as helping his children and others toward growth and maturity or achievement of significant professional or occupational gains. People who lived good, productive lives need and deserve gratitude and the feeling that their lives have been blessed. Most of my disturbed geriatric patients become less restless and agitated when I emphasize those ideas repeatedly in individual psychotherapy. It is the rare elderly person who cannot in such psychotherapy perceive some aspect of his life in a highly positive manner, in which he can see himself as having contributed something of value to a significant person in his life.

Retirement, whether voluntary or involuntary, is sometimes a tremendous blow to a person's self-concept. Life must remain meaningful and purposeful; the elderly person must work for, live for, and hope for somebody or something. As long as an elderly person has the hope of some achievement, whether it be intellectual, spiritual, emotional, or practical, he can maintain his self-esteem and handle other concerns and fears more realistically. Goal-directed attitudes not only will reduce the fear of death and dying but will help the elderly person to gain a positive image of himself and his role in the world around him. To convey hope, re-establish confidence, and overcome undue fear of death have to be our therapeutic goals.

REFERENCES

1. BIRREN, J. E.: Principles of research on aging. In *Handbook of Aging and the Individual. Psychological and Biological Aspects,* edited by J. E. Birren. Chicago, U. of Chicago, 1959.
2. BUSSE, E. W.: Administration of the interdisciplinary research team. *J. Med. Educ. 40*:832-839, 1965.
3. WOLFF, K.: *The Biological, Sociological and Psychological Aspects of Aging.* Springfield, Thomas, 1959.
4. BORTZ, E. L.: Retirement and the individual. *J. Amer. Geriat. Soc., XVI*(1):1-15, 1968.
5. *Aging.* U. S. Dept. of Health, Education and Welfare. Washington, D.C., U. S. Government Printing Office, May 1969.
6. SHELDON, H. D.: The changing demographic profile. In *Handbook of Social Gerontology, Societal Aspects of Aging,* edited by C. Tibbitts. Chicago, U. of Chicago, 1960.
7. LANSING, A. I.: Some physiological aspects of aging. *Physiol. Rev., 31*:274-284, 1951.
8. LANSING, A. I.: General physiology. In *Cowdry's Problems of Aging,* 3rd Ed., edited by A. I. Lansing. Baltimore, Williams and Wilkins, 1952.
9. HIMWICH, H. E., and HIMWICH, W. A.: Brain metabolism in relation to aging. In *The Neurologic and Psychiatric Aspects of the Disorders of Aging.* Baltimore, Williams and Wilkins, 1956.
10. HIMWICH, W. A., and HIMWICH, H. E.: Brain composition during the whole life span. *Geriatrics, 12*:19-27, 1957.
11. BUERGER, M.: Biomorphose oder Gerontologie? *Z. Alternsforsch., 10*:279-283, 1957.
12. HEINRICH, A.: Beitraege zur Physiology des Alterns. *Z. Ges. Exp. Med., 96*:722-728, 1935.
13. BUERGER, M.: Die Biomorphose des menschlichen Gehirns im Lichte seines wechselnden Nukleinsaüre und Gangliosidgehalts. *Z. Alternsforsch., 10*:283-288, 1957.
14. NIKITIN, W. N., Golubizka and others: The biochemical age change of the denervative organs. *Uchen Zapiski, Kharkov Univ., 68*:79-99, 1956.

15. Himwich, H. E., and Himwich, W. A.: Brain metabolism in relation to aging. In *The Neurologic and Psychiatric Aspects of the Disorders of Aging*. Baltimore, Williams and Wilkins, 1956.

16. Kety, S. S.: Human cerebral blood flow oxygen consumption as related to aging. In *The Neurologic and Psychiatric Aspects of the Disorders of Aging*. Baltimore, Williams and Wilkins, 1956.

17. Kety, S. S.: Circulation and metabolism of the human brain in health and disease. *Amer. J. Med., 8*:205, 1950.

18. Sobel, H.: Aging theory—Cellular and extracellular modalities. In *Contributions to the Psycho-Biology of Aging,* edited by R. Kastenbaum. New York, Springer, 1965.

19. Schwartz, P. H.: Pathoanatomic alterations in the aged. *Psychosomatics,* Section 2:12-20, July-August 1967.

20. Lowry, O. H., and Hastings, A. B.: Quantitative histochemical changes in aging. In *Cowdry's Problems of Aging,* 3rd Ed., edited by A. I. Lansing. Baltimore, Williams and Wilkins, 1952.

21. Freeman, J. T.: *Clinical Features of the Older Patient,* edited by J. T. Freeman. Springfield, Thomas, 1964, p. 37.

22. Shock, N. W.: Age changes in some physiologic processes. *Geriatrics, 12*:40-48, 1957.

23. Shock, N. W.: *Trends in Gerontology,* 2nd Ed. Stanford, Stanford U., 1957.

24. Verzár, F.: The growth of a new science. *Triangle, 8*(8):293-303, 1968.

25. Shock, N. W.: Aging of homeostatic mechanisms. In *Cowdry's Problems of Aging,* 3rd Ed., edited by A. I. Lansing. Baltimore, Williams and Wilkins, 1952.

26. McFarland, R. A.: Experimental evidence of the relationship between aging and oxygen want: In search of a theory of aging. *Ergonomics, 6*:339-366, 1963.

27. Geschickter, C. F.: Some fundamental aspects of the aging process. In V.A. Prospectus, *Research in Aging*. Washington, D.C., U.S. Government Printing Office, 1959.

28. Barnes, R. H., Busse, E. W., and Friedman, E. L.: The psychological functioning of aged individuals with normal and abnormal electroencephalograms. II. A study of hospitalized individuals. *J. Nerv. Ment. Dis., 124*:585-593, 1956.

29. Busse, E. W., and Obrist, W. D.: Pre-senescent Electroencephalographic changes in normal subjects. *J. Geront. 20*(3):315-320, 1965.

30. STIEGLITZ, E. J.: Principles of geriatric medicine. In *Geriatric Medicine*, 3rd Ed., edited by E. J. Stieglitz. Philadelphia, Lippincott, 1954.

31. STIEGLITZ, E. J.: Foundation of geriatric medicine. In *Geriatric Medicine*, 3rd Ed., edited by E. J. Stieglitz. Philadelphia, Lippincott, 1954.

32. FREEMAN, J. T.: The mechanisms of stress and the forces of senescence. *J. Amer. Geriat. Soc., 7*:71-78, 1959.

33. McGAVACK, T. H.: Aging as seen by the endocrinologist. *Geriatrics, 18*(3):181-191, 1963.

34. BERRY, R. G.: Neuropathologic aspects of aging. *Geriatrics, 18*(3): 202-210, 1963.

35. SCHLEZINGER, N. S.: Degenerative and infectious disorders. *Geriatrics, 18*(3):197-201, 1963.

36. O'LEARY, J. L.: Aging in the nervous system. In *Cowdry's Problems of Aging*, 3rd Ed., edited by A. I. Lansing. Baltimore, Williams and Wilkins, 1952.

37. WEXBERG, L. E.: Discussion. In Kolb, L.: The psychiatric significance of aging as a public health problem. In *Mental Health in Later Maturity*. Federal Security Agency, U. S. Public Health Service, Supplement No. 168, p. 19.

38. KALLMANN, F. J.: Heredity and aging. In *The Newsletter of the Gerontological Society, 4*:5, 1957.

39. KALLMANN, F. J.: The genetics of aging. In *The Neurologic and Psychiatric Aspects of the Disorders of Aging*. Baltimore, Williams and Wilkins, 1956.

40. CURTIS, H. J.: The somatic mutation theory of aging. *In Contributions to the Psycho-Biology of Aging*, edited by R. Kastenbaum. New York, Springer, 1965.

41. CURTIS, H. J.: *Biological Mechanisms of Aging*. Springfield, Thomas, 1966.

42. COMFORT, A.: *The Biology of Senescence*. London, Routlege and Kegan, Paul, 1956.

43. SELYE, H., and PRIORESCHI: In *Aging. Some Social and Biological Aspects*, edited by N. W. Shock. Washington, D. C., American Association for the Advancement of Science, 1960.

44. Jarvik, L. F.: Senescence and chromosomal changes. *Lancet, 1*: 114-115, 1963.

45. WALFORD, R. L.: Changes in immunological status with advancing Age. In *Contributions to the Psycho-Biology of Aging*, edited by R. Kastenbaum. New York, Springer, 1965.

46. REICHEL, W.: The biology of aging. *J. Amer. Geriat. Soc., XIV* (5) : 431-446, 1966.

47. STARE, F. J.: Nutrition and aging. *J. Amer. Geriat. Soc., 3*:767-777, 1955.

48. McCAY, C. M.: Chemical aspects of aging and the effect of diet upon aging. In *Cowdry's Problems of Aging*, 3rd Ed. edited by A. I. Lansing. Baltimore, Williams and Wilkins, 1952.

49. SELYE, H.: *The Stress of Life*. New York, McGraw-Hill, 1956.

50. SELYE, H.: *The Physiology and Pathology of Exposure to Stress*. Montreal, Acta, 1950.

51. Whipple, R. O.: Discussion on biological processes in aging. *Science, 141*:686, 1963.

52. WENDKOS, M. H., and WOLFF, K.: Emotional correlates of angina pectoris. *J. Amer. Geriat. Soc., 16* (8) :845-858, 1968.

53. BURGESS, E. W.: The older generation and the family. In *The New Frontiers of Aging*, edited by W. Donahue and C. Tibbitts. Ann Arbor, U. of Michigan, 1957.

54. BURGESS, E. W.: *Round Table Meeting on Psychiatric Factors in Aging. Annual Meeting*, A.P.A., May 14, 1957, Chicago, Ill.

55. RICHARDSON, I. M.: Retirement: A social-medical study of 244 men. *Scot. Med. J., 1*:381-391, 1956.

56. WHITE, E. B.: A stratagem for retirement. *Holiday*, March 1956, pp. 84-87.

57. SHOCK, N. W.: *Trends in Gerontology*, 2nd Ed. Stanford, Stanford U. 1957.

58. DONAHUE, W.: Emerging principles and concepts: A summary. In *The New Frontiers of Aging*, edited by W. Donahue and C. Tibbitts. Ann Arbor, U. of Michigan, 1957.

59. STREIB, G. F., and THOMPSON, W. E.: Personal and Social Adjustment in Retirement. In: *The New Frontiers of Aging*, edited by W. Donahue and C. Tibbitts. Ann Arbor, U. of Michigan, 1957.

60. TIBBITTS, C.: Retirement problems in American society. *Amer. J. Sociol. 59*:301-308, 1954.

61. GIBERSON, L. G.: Industrial aspects of aging personnel. In *Mental Health in Later Maturity*, Federal Security Agency, U. S. Public Health Service, Supplement No. 168, p. 22.

62. FRANK, L. K.: Discussion. In *Old Age and Aging. Amer. J. Orthopsychiat. 10*:39-42, 1940.

63. TARTLER, R.: The older person in family, community and society. In *Process of Aging*, edited by R. H. Williams, C. Tibbitts and

W. Donahue. New York, Atherton (Division of Prentice-Hall), 1963, Ch. 31.

64. RIESMAN, D.: *The Lonely Crowd.* New York, Doubleday, 1956.

65. BURGESS, E. W.: The transition from extended families to nuclear families. In *Process of Aging,* edited by R. H. Williams, C. Tibbitts and W. Donahue. New York, Atherton (Division of Prentice-Hall), 1963, Ch. 32.

66. BURGESS, E. W.: *Aging in Western Societies,* edited by E. W. Burgess. Chicago, U. of Chicago, 1960.

67. WOLFF, K.: Family conflicts and Aging. *Northwest Med. 66*:50-55, 1967.

68. MENNINGER, K. A.: *Love Against Hate.* New York, Harcourt, 1942.

69. FREUD, S.: *Three Contributions to the Theory of Sex,* 4th Ed. New York, Nervous and Mental Diseases Publishers, 1930.

70. STREIB, G. F., and THOMPSON, W. E.: The older person in a family context. In *Handbook of Social Gerontology,* edited by C. Tibbitts. Chicago, U. of Chicago, 1960.

71. DAVIS, K.: The sociology of parent-youth conflict. *Amer. Sociol. Rev., 4*:523-535, 1940.

72. YARROW, M. R., BLANK, P., WUINN, O. W., YOUMANS, E. G., and STEIN, JR.: Social psychological characteristics of old age. In *Human Aging,* edited by J. E. Birren. U. S. Department of Health, Education and Welfare, Public Health Service Publication No. 986, 1963.

73. BUSSE, E. W.: The treatment of hypochondriasis. *Tri-State Med. J., 2*:7-12, 1954.

74. CUMMINGS, E., and HENRY, W. E.: *Growing Old, the Process of Disengagement.* New York, Basic Books, 1961.

75. KASTENBAUM, R.: Engrossment and perspective in later life: A developmental field approach. In *Thoughts on Old Age, edited* by R. Kastenbaum. New York, Springer, 1964.

76. HAVIGHURST, R. J.: Personality and patterns of aging. *Gerontologist, 8*(1), Part II:20-23, 1968.

77. HAVIGHURST, R. J.: Successful aging. *Gerontologist, 1*:1, 1961.

78. BREHM, H. P.: Sociology and aging: Orientation and research. *Gerontologist, 8*(1), Part II:24-31, 1968.

79. CAVAN, R. S.: Self and role in adjustment during old age. In *Human Behavior and Social Processes,* edited by A.M. Rose. Boston, Houghton Mifflin, 1962.

80. VIDEBECK, R., and KNOW, A. B.: Alternative participatory responses

to aging. In *Older People and Their Social World,* edited by A. M. Rose and W. A. Peterson. Philadelphia, Davis, 1965.

81. BORTZ, E. L.: Retirement and the individual. *J. Amer. Geriat. Soc., XVI*(1):1-15, 1968.

82. KOBRYNSKI, B.: A new look at geriatric care. *J. Amer. Geriat. Soc., XVI*(10):1114-1125, 1968.

83. KUTNER, B.: Socio-economic impact of aging. *J. Amer. Geriat. Soc., 14*(1):33-40, 1966.

84. LINDEN, M. E.: Relationship between social attitudes toward aging and the delinquencies of youth. Presented at the First Pan-American Congress on Gerontology, Mexico City, September 18, 1956. *Amer. J. Psychiat. 144*:444-448, 1957.

85. GITELSON, M.: The emotional problems of elderly people. *Geriatrics, 3*:135-150, 1948.

86. KAPLAN, O. J.: *Studies in the Psychopathology of Later Life.* Berkeley, U. of California Library, 1940.

87. OVERHOLZER, W.: *Orientation, Mental Health in Later Maturity.* U.S. Public Health Reports, Supplement No. 168, 1942.

88. JONES, H. E.: Notes on the study of mental abilities in maturity and later maturity. In *Research on Aging.* Proceedings of a Conference, August 1950, University of California. New York, Social Science Research Council, 1950.

89. KUHLEN, R. G.: Age trends in adjustment during the adult years as reflected in happiness ratings. *Amer. J. Psychol., 3*:307, 1948.

90. HAVIGHURST, R. J.: Personal and social adjustment in old age. In *The New Frontiers of Aging,* edited by W. Donahue and C. Tibbitts. Ann Arbor, U. of Michigan, 1957.

91. HAVIGHURST, R. J.: Roles and status of old people. In *Cowdry's Problems of Aging,* 3rd Ed., edited by A. I. Lansing. Baltimore, Williams and Wilkins, 1952.

92. MEERLOO, J. A. M.: Transference and resistance in geriatric psychotherapy. *Psychoanal. Rev., 42*:1, 1955.

93. GOLDFARB, A. I.: Psychiatric problems of old age. *New York J. Med., 55*:494-500, 1955.

94. GOLDFARB, A. I., and TURNER, H.: Psychotherapy of aged persons. *Amer. J. Psychiat., 109*:916-921, 1953.

95. GOLDFARB, A. I.: Psychotherapy of aged persons. *Psychoanal. Rev., 42*:180-187, 1955.
aging period. *Geriatrics, 12*:123-129, 1957.

96. GERTY, F.: Importance of individualization of treatment in the

97. MASSERMAN, J. H.: The psychodynamics of aging. *Geriatrics, 12*: 115-122, 1957.

98. BUSSE, E. W.: Mental health in advanced maturity. In *The New Frontiers of Aging*, edited by W. Donahue and C. Tibbitts. Ann Arbor, U. of Michigan, 1957.

99. BUSSE, E. W.: The treatment of hypochondriasis. *Tri-State Med. J., 2*:7-12, 1954.

100. SCHIELE, B. C.: *Panel Discussion on Tranquilizing Drugs in the Clinical Management of Mental Disease in Geriatric Patients.* The American Geriatric Society and The American Academy of General Practice, New York City, Nov. 19, 1956.

101. DUNBAR, F: Immunity to the afflictions of old age. *J. Amer. Geriat. Soc., 5*:982-996, 1957.

102. LIEBMAN, S.: *Stress Situations.* Philadelphia and Montreal, Lippincott, 1955.

103. GROTJAHN, M.: Analytic psychotherapy with the elderly. *Psychoanal. Rev., 42*:419-427, 1955.

104. KAUFMAN, M. R.: Psychoanalysis in later life depressions. *Psychoanal. Quart., 6*:308-335, 1937.

105. SIMON, A.: Emotional problems of women — The mature years and beyond. *Psychosomatics, IX*(4):12-16, 1968.

106. BEREZIN, M. A.: Introduction. *In Geriatric Psychiatry. Grief, Loss and Emotional Disorders in the Aging Process*, edited by M. A. Berezin and S. H. Cath. New York, Int. Univs. Press, 1965, p. 18.

107. BUTLER, R. N.: Aspects of survival and adaptation in human aging. *Amer. J. Psychiat., 123*(10):1233-1243, 1967.

108. DEUTSCH, H.: *The Psychology of Women, Vol. II.* New York, Grune and Stratton, 1945.

109. WEINBERG, J.: Sexual expression in late life. *Amer. J. Psychiat. 126*(5), 1969.

110. DENBER, H. C. B.: Sexual problems in the mature female. *Psychosomatics, IX*(4), Section 2:40-43, 1968

111. VERWOERDT, A., PFEIFFER, E., and WANG, H. S.: Sexual behavior in senescence. *Geriatrics, 24*(2):137-154, 1969.

112. HAMILTON, G. V.: Changes in personality and psychosexual phenomena. In *Cowdry's Problems of Aging*, 2nd Ed. Baltimore, Williams and Wilkins, 1942.

113. SCHILDER, P.: Psychiatric aspects of old age and aging. *Amer. J. Orthopsychiat. 10*:62-69, 1940.

114. BOWMAN, K. M.: Mental adjustment of physical changes with aging. *Geriatrics, 2*:139-145, 1956.

115. EBAUGH, F. G.: Age introduces stress into the family. *Geriatrics,* 2:146-150, 1956.

116. DOVENMUEHLE, R. H., and VERWOERDT, A.: Physical illness and depressive symptomatology. II. Factors of length and severity of illness and frequency of hospitalization. *J. Geront. 18*(3): 260-266, 1963.

117. MALAMUD, W.: The psychopathology of aging. In *The Neurologic and Psychiatric Aspects of the Disorders of Aging.* Baltimore, Williams and Wilkins, 1956.

118. MILES, W. R.: Correlation of reaction and coordination speed with age in adults. *Amer. J. Psychol., 43*:377, 1931.

119. WECHSLER, D.: *The Measurement of Adult Intelligence.* Baltimore, Williams and Wilkins, 1951.

120. GILBERT, J. G.: Discussion in: Old age and aging. *Amer. J. Orthopsychiat., 10*:59, 1940.

121. GRANICK, S.: The psychology of senility. A review. *J. Geront., 5*: 44, 1950.

122. BIRREN, J. E.: Sensation, perception and modification of behavior in relation to the process of aging. In *The Process of Aging in the Nervous System,* J. E. Birren, H. A. Imus and W. F. Windle. Springfield, Thomas, 1959.

123. ROSE, A. M.: A current theoretical issue in social gerontology. In *Older People and their Social World,* edited by A. M. Rose and W. A. Peterson. Philadelphia, Davis, 1965, pp. 359-366.

124. WAHL, C. W.: The fear of death. In *The Meaning of Death,* edited by H. Feifel. New York, McGraw-Hill, 1959, pp. 16-29.

125. MEERLOO, J. A.: Transference and resistance in geriatric psychotherapy. *Psychoanal. Rev., 42*:72-82, 1955.

126. FEIFEL, H.: Attitudes toward death in some normal and mentally ill populations. In *The Meaning of Death,* edited by H. Feifel. New York, McGraw-Hill, 1959, pp. 114-130.

127. HUTSCHNECKER, A. A.: Personality factors in dying patients. In *The Meaning of Death,* edited by H. Feifel. New York, McGraw-Hill, 1959, pp. 237-250.

128. WOLFF, K.: *Geriatric Psychiatry.* Springfield, Thomas, 1963.

129. WOLFF, K.: Personality type and reaction toward aging and death. *Geriatrics, 21*:189-192, 1966.

130. BRACELAND, F. J.: The role of the psychiatrist in rehabilitation. *J.A.M.A.,* September 21, 1957.

131. MENNINGER, K., MAYMAN, M., and PRUYSER, P.: *The Vital Balance.* New York, Viking, 1963.

132. FRANKL, V. E.: *Man's Search for Meaning.* New York, Washington Square Press, 1963.
133. GOLDFARB, A.: Prevalence of psychiatric disorders in metropolitan old age and nursing homes. *J. Amer. Geriat. Soc., X*:1, 1962.
134. EPSTEIN, L. J., and SIMON, A.: Organic brain syndrome in the elderly. *Geriatrics, 22*(2):145-150, 1967.
135. SMIGEL, J. D., SERHUS, L. N., and BARMAK, S.: Metrazol. Its place in geriatric psychiatry. *J. Med. Soc. New Jersey, 50*:248-252, 1953.
136. SEIDEL, H., SILVER, A. A., and NAGEL, H.: Effects of metrazol and nicotinamide on psychic and mental disorders in the geriatric patient. *J. Amer. Geriat. Soc.,* 1:280-282, 1953.
137. LEVY, S.: Pharmacological treatment of aged patients in a state mental hospital. *J.A.M.A., 153*:1260-1265, 1953.
138. FONG, TH. C. C.: Oral Metrazol therapy in psychoses with cerebral arteriosclerosis. *J. Amer. Geriat. Soc.,* 1:662-664, 1953.
139. LINDEN, M. E., COURTNEY, D., and HOWLAND, A. O.: Interdisciplinary research in the use of oral pentylenetetrazol (Metrazol) in the emotional disorders of the aged. *J. Amer. Geriat. Soc.,* 6(4):380-399, 1956.
140. WOLFF, K.: Treatment of the geriatric patient in a mental hospital, *J. Amer. Geriat. Soc.,* 4:472, 1956.
141. TENNENT, J. J.: Oral pentylenetetrazol in geriatric practice. *Geriatrics, 15*(2):848-851, 1960.
142. HIMWICH, H. E., WOLFF, K., HUNSICKER, A. L., and HIMWICH, W. A.: Some behavioral effects associated with feeding sodium glutamate to patients with psychiatric disorders. *J. Nerv. Ment. Dis., 121*(1):40-49, 1955.
143. KATZ, E. M., and KOWALICZKO, Z.: A clinical study on the effect of l'glutavite on mental function and behavior of elderly chronically sick patients. *Intern. Record of Medicine and General Practice Clinics, 169*:596-606, 1956.
144. WOLFF, K.: L'glutavite, clinical effects on geriatric patients in a psychiatric hospital. *J. Kansas Med. Soc., LIX*:7:310, 1958.
145. CURRIER, R. D., SMITH, E. M., STEININGER, E. H., and STEININGER, M.: A study of l'glutavite as compared to a Ritalin combination in the chronic brain syndrome. *Geriatrics, 16*(6):311-316, 1961.
146. GASSTER, M.: Clinical experience with l'glutavite in aged patients with behavior problems and memory defects. *J. Amer. Geriat. Soc., IX*(5):370, 1961.

147. ASLAN, A.: Recent experiences on the rejuvenating action of Novocain (H₃), together with experimental, clinical and statistical findings. In *Research on Novocain Therapy in Old Age.* New York, Consultants Bureau, 1959, p. 28.

148. KOHLER, U., and MANPEL, F.: Procaine. *Therapiewoche,* 8:28-30, 1957.

149. GERICKE, O. L., LOBB, L. G., and PARDOLL, D. H.: An evaluation of procaine in geriatric patients in a mental hospital. *J. Clin. Exp. Psychopath.,* 22(1):18-33, 1961.

150. SMIGEL, J. O.: *et al.*: H-3 (Procaine Hydrochloride) Therapy in Aging Institutionalized Patients: An Interim Report, *J. Amer. Geriat. Soc.,* 7(10):785-794, 1960.

151. CASHMAN, M. D., and LAWES, T. G. G.: A controlled study of Gerioptil. *Brit. Med. J.,* 554-556, February 1961.

152. WOLFF, K. and KLUGLER, J.: The use of Novocaine Therapy for geriatric patients. Unpublished study.

153. JONES, R. T.: Drug therapy in the aged. *Cooperative Chemotherapy Studies in Psychiatry,* 5:269, 1960 (V.A., Washington, D.C.).

154. WOLFF, K.: Individual psychotherapy with geriatric patients. *Dis. Nerv. Syst.,* 24(11), 1963.

155. BUSSE, E. W.: Psychopathology. In *Handbook of Aging and the Individual,* edited by J. E. Birren. Chicago, U. of Chicago, 1959.

156. LEVIN, S.: Depression in the aged: A study of the salient external factors. In *Selected Papers from the First Annual Symposium on Old Age.* Framingham, Mass., Cushing Hospital, May 22, 1963.

157. GARDNER, E. A., BAHN, A. K., and MACK, J.: Suicide and psychiatric care in the aging. *Arch. Gen. Psychiat. 10*:547-553, 1964.

158. ROTH, M.: Mental health problems of aging and the aged. *Bull. W.H.O., 21*:527, 1959.

159. JONES, H. E., and KAPLAN, O. J.: Psychological aspects of mental disorders in later life. In *Mental Disorders in Later Life,* 2nd Ed., edited by O. J. Kaplan. Stanford, Stanford, U., 1956, p. 141.

160. Coronary-prone patient identified. New York, *The American Heart Association.* Reprinted by the *A.M.A. News,* February 26, 1968.

161. MULCAHY, R., *et al.*: (Dept. of Med., Univ. Col., Dublin, Ireland) Coronary heart disease in women. Study of risk factors in 100 patients less than 60 years of age. *Circulation, 36*:577-586, 1967.

162. WOLFE, T. P.: Dynamic aspects of cardiovascular symptomatology. *Amer. J. Psychiat.*, *91*:563, 1934.

163. DUNBAR, F.: *Emotions and Bodily Changes*, 3rd Ed. New York, Columbia, 1947.

164. ARLOW, J. A.: Anxiety patterns in angina pectoris, *Psychosom. Med.*, *XIV*(6):461-468, 1952.

165. RUSSEK, H. I., and ZOHMAN, B. L.: Relative significance of heredity, diet, and occupational stress in coronary heart disease of young adults based on an analysis of 100 patients between the ages of 25 and 40 years and a similar group of 100 normal control subjects. *Amer. J. Med. Sci.*, *235*:266, 1958.

166. FRIEDMAN, M., and ROSEMAN, R. H.: Association of specific overt behavior pattern with blood and cardiovascular findings. *J.A.M.A.*, *169*:1286,, 1959.

167. BELLAK, L., and HASELKORN, F.: Psychological aspects of cardiac illness and rehabilitation. *Social Casework*, *37*:483-489, 1956.

168. HAU, T. F., and RUEPPEL, A.: Psychodynamics in coronary disease (Mediz. Universitätsklinik, Freiburg, Germany). *Med. Klin.*, *61*:368-371, 1966.

169. IBRAHIM, M. A., *et al.*: Personality traits and coronary heart disease. *J. Chronic Dis.*, *19*:255, 1966.

170. BAKKER, C. B.: Psychological factors in angina pectoris. *Psychosomatics*, *VIII*(1):43-49, 1967.

171. WENDKOS, M. H., and WOLFF, K.: Emotional correlates of angina pectoris. *J. Amer. Geriat. Soc.*, *16*(8):845-858, 1968.

172. FREUD, S.: On psychotherapy. In *Collected Papers, Vol. 1*. London, Hogarth, 1924.

173. FENICHEL, O.: *The Psychoanalytic Theory of Neurosis*. New York, Norton, 1945.

174. ABRAHAM, K.: The applicability of psychoanalytic treatment to patients at an advanced age. In *Selected Papers of Psychoanalysis*. London, Hogarth, 1949.

175. JELLIFFEE, S. E.: The old age factor in psychoanalytic therapy. *Med. J. Rec.*, *121*:7-12, 1925.

176. ALEXANDER, F. G., and FRENCH, T. M.: *Psychoanalytic Therapy, Principles and Applications*. New York, Ronald, 1946.

177. KAUFMAN, M. R.: Old age and aging. The psychoanalytic point of view. *Amer. J. Orthopsychiat.*, 10, 1940.

178. ALEXANDER, F. G., and FRENCH, T. M.: *Psychoanalytic Therapy, Principles and Applications*. New York, Ronald, 1946.

179. GROTJAHN, M.: Psychoanalytic investigation of a seventy-one-year-

old man with senile dementia. *Psychoanal. Quart. 9*:80-97, 1940.

180. MEERLOO, J. A. M.: Psychotherapy with elderly people. *Geriatrics, 10*:583, 1955.

181. WEINBERG, J.: Psychotherapy of the aged person. In *The Neurological and Psychiatric Aspects of the Disorders of Aging,* edited by J. E. Moore, H. H. Merritt and R. J. Masselink. Baltimore, Williams and Wilkins, 1956.

182. WAYNE, G. J.: Psychotherapy in senescence. *Ann. West. Med. Surg. 6*:88, 1952.

183. GOLDFARB, A. I.:Psychotherapy of aged persons. Orientation of staff in a home for the aged. *Ment. Hyg.* 37:1, 1953.

184. BUTLER, R. N.: Intensive psychotherapy for the hospitalized aged. *Geriatrics, 15*:644, 1960.

185. POST, F.: *The Clinical Psychiatry of Late Life.* Oxford and New York, Pergamon, 1965.

186. WOLFF, K.: Individual psychotherapy with geriatric patients. *Dis. Nerv. Syst., 24*(11) :1-4, 1963.

187. WOLFF, K.: Individual psychotherapy with geriatric patients. *Dis. Nerv. Syst., 24*(11) :1-4, 1963.

188. SILVER, A.: Group psychotherapy with senile psychotic women. *Geriatrics, 5*:147, 1950.

189. SCHWARTZ, E. D., and GOODMAN, J. I.: Group therapy of obesity in elderly diabetics. *Geriatrics, 7*:280, 1952.

190. BENAIM, S.: Group psychotherapy within a geriatric unit: An experiment. *Int. J. Soc. Psychiat., III*:2, 1957.

191. LINDEN, M. E.: Group psychotherapy with institutionalized senile women. II. Study in gerontologic human relations. *Int. J. Group Psychother.,* 13, 1953.

192. RECHTSCHAFFEN, A., ATKINSON, S., and FREEMAN, J. G.: An intensive treatment program for state hospital geriatric patients. *Geriatrics, 9*:28, 1954.

193. WOLFF, K.: Group psychotherapy with geriatric patients in a psychiatric hospital. *Psychiatric Studies and Projects, 3*(2), February 1963 (American Psychiatric Association, Washington, D.C.).

194. KNUDSON, A. B. C.: Physical medicine and rehabilitation. Application to geriatric problems. *J. Amer. Geriat. Soc.,* II:9, 1954.

195. FERDERBER, M. B.: Aspects of rehabilitation of the aged. *J.A.M.A., 162*:11, 1956.

196. BLUSTEIN, H.: A rehabilitation program for geriatric patients. *J. Amer. Geriat. Soc., VII*:3, 1960.

197. PEARMAN, H., and NEUMAN, N.: Work oriented occupational therapy for the geriatric patient. *Amer. J. Occup. Ther.*, 22:263, 1968.

198. FIDLER, G. S., and FIDLER, J. W.: *Psychiatric Occupational Therapy.* New York, Macmillan, 1954.

199. MENNINGER, W. C.: Psychological Aspects of Hobbies. *Amer. J. Psychiat.* 99:1, 1942.

200. GUMPERT, M.: Geriatrics and social work. Presented to the Institute on Group Work and Recreation with the Aged. Cleveland, Ohio, Western Reserve Univ., April 16, 1953.

201. MARTIN, A. R.: The fear of relaxation and leisure. *Amer. J. Psychoanal.*, *XI*:1, 1951.

202. HUTCHINSON, E. D.: The nature of insight. *Psychiatry, IV*, 1941.

203. MENNINGER, W. C.: Psychological aspects of hobbies. *Amer. J. Psychiat.* 99:1, 1942.

204. BORTZ, E. L.: Education, aging and meaningful survival. *J. Amer. Geriat. Soc., IX*(5):329-348, 1961.

205. BOXBERGER, R., and COTTER, V. W.: Music therapy for geriatric patients. In *Music in Therapy*, edited by E. T. Gaston. New York, Macmillan, 1968.

206. MASON, A. S.: The hospital service clinic — A work modality for the geriatric mental patient. *J. Amer. Geriat. Soc., 13*(6): 545-549, 1965.

207. WINICK, W.: *Industry in the Hospital, Mental Rehabilitation Through Work.* Springfield, Thomas, 1967.

208. BLUSTEIN, H.: A rehabilitation program for geriatric patients. *J. Amer. Geriat. Soc., VII*:3, 1960.

209. ACKERMAN, N. W.: *The Psychodynamics of Family Life.* Basic Books, 1958.

210. COSIN, L. Z.: Geriatric day hospital for psychiatric patients. *Med. World, 87*:214-219, 1957.

211. COSIN, L. Z.: Current therapeutic and psychotherapeutic concepts for the geriatric patient. In *Progress in Psychotherapy*, edited by J. H. Masserman and J. L. Moreno. New York, Grune and Stratton, 1957.

212. POLNER, W.: Day hospital for geriatric patients. *Geriatrics, 16*:2, 1961.

213. ANDERSON, C. J., PORRATA, E., *et al.*: A multidisciplinary study of the psychogeriatric patient. *Geriatrics, 23*(2):105-113, 1968.

214. KAPLAN, J.: The day center and the day care center. *Geriatrics, 12*:4, 1957.

215. SAVITZ, H. A.: Humanizing institutional care for the aged. *J. Amer. Geriat. Soc., 15*(2):203-210, 1967.

216. DOMINICK, J. R., GREENBLATT, D. L., and STOTSKY, B. A.: The adjustment of aged persons in nursing homes. *J. Amer. Geriat. Soc., 16*(1):63-77, 1968.

217. LINN, M.W., and GUREL, L.: Initial reactions to nursing home placement. *J. Amer. Geriat. Soc., 17*(2), 1969.

218. STOTSKY, B.: The psychiatric patient in the nursing home. *J. Amer. Geriat. Soc., 14*(7):735-747, 1966.

219. GOLDFARB, A. I.: Prediction of mortality in the aged, a seven-year follow-up. Paper presented at the 7th Internat. Cong. on Mental Health, London, England, August 1968.

220. LEEDS, M.: *Aging in Indiana.* Indianapolis, The Indiana State Commission on the Aging and Aged, Sept. 1960.

221. LEVINE, H. A.: Community programs for the elderly. Philadelphia, *The Annals of the American Academy of Political and Social Science,* January 1952.

222. KUBIE, S. H., and LANDAU, G.: *Groupwork with the Aged.* New York, Int. Univs. Press, 1953.

223. FENDELL, N.: A new role for foster grandparents. Paper presented at the 7th Internat. Cong. on Mental Health, London, England, August 1968.

224. DANIELS, R. S., and KAHN, R. L.: Community mental health and programs for the aged. *Geriatrics, 23*(3):121-125, 1968.

225. Personal observation. See also Chandler, R.: Fort Logan Mental Health Geriatric Service. *Denver Med. Bull., 57*:44, 1967.

226. MILLER, M. B.: The chronically ill aged, family conflict, and family medicine. *J. Amer. Geriat. Soc., 17*(10):950-961, 1969.

227. JONES, M.: *Social Psychiatry.* Springfield, Thomas, 1962.

228. ACKERMAN, N. W.: *The Psychodynamics of Family Life.* New York, Basic Books, 1958.

229. LIEBMAN, S.: *The Emotional Forces in the Family,* edited by S. Liebman. Philadelphia, Lippincott, 1959.

230. WOLFF, K.: Family conflicts and aging. *Northwest Med. 66*:50-55, 1967.

231. HAVIGHURST, R. J.: Successful aging. *Gerontologist, 1*:1, 1961.

232. COSIN, L.: Physiotherapy in Geriatric rehabilitation. *Permanente Fdn. Med. Bull., 10*:337, 1953.

233. RUSK, H. A., and DASCO, M. M.: Rehabilitation in the aged. *Bull. N.Y. Acad. Med., 32*:725-733, 1956.

234. BONNER, C. D.: Rehabilitation instead of bed rest. *Geriatrics,* 24(6):109-118, 1969.

235. KNUDSON, A. B. C.: Rehabilitation of the chronically ill in the Veterans Administration. *J.A.M.A., 162*:11, 1956.

236. BRACELAND, F. J.: The role of the psychiatrist in rehabilitation. *J.A.M.A.,* September 21, 1957.

237. TIMM, O. K.: Modern trends in psychiatric care of the geriatric patient. *J. Amer. Geriat. Soc., 13*(12):1025-1031, 1965.

238. BUSSE, E. W., and co-workers: Geriatrics today. An overview. *Amer. J. Psychiat., 123*:1226-1233, 1967.

239. DAVIS, R. W.: Activity therapy in a geriatric setting. *J. Amer. Geriat. Soc., 15*(12):1144-1151, 1967.

240. FILER, R., and O'CONNELL, D.: Motivation of aged persons. *J. Geront., 19*:15-22, 1964.

241. FOLSOM, J. C.:The attitude program. A springboard for progress. *Ment. Hosp. 16*(11):45-47, 1965.

242. WOLFF, K.: Observations on depression and suicide in the geriatric patient. In *Patterns of Self-Destruction — Depression and Suicide.* Springfield, Thomas, 1970.

243. COHEN, D.: Research problems and concepts in the study of aging. *Gerontologist, 7*(2):13-19, 1967.

244. REYNA, L. J.: Conditioning therapies, learning theory and research. In *The Conditioning Therapies,* edited by J. Wolpe, A. Salter and L. J. Reyna. New York, Holt, Rinehart and Winston, 1964.

245. REVUSKY, S. H., and co-workers: Automated training of social relationships in extremely withdrawn patients. *V.A. Newsletter in Res. Psychol. 5*:32-35, 1963.

246. GOLDFARB, A. I.: The dependency contract as an aid to psychiatric care of the aged. In *Scientific proceedings, The 123rd Annual Meeting of the A.P.A.,* 1963, pp. 102-103.

247. SIMON, A.: The geriatric mentally ill. *The Gerontologist, 8*(2):7-15, 1968.

248. KORSON, S. M.: From custodial care to intensive treatment of the geriatric patient. *J. Amer. Geriat. Soc., 16*(10):1107-1113, 1968.

249. KOBRYNSKI, B.: A new look at geriatric care. *J. Amer. Geriat. Soc., 16*(10):1114-1125, 1968.

NAME INDEX

SUBJECT INDEX